NVQ Engineering
Level 2

Mandatory Units

NVQ Engineering
Level 2

Mandatory Units

David Salmon
Lecturer, Royal Forest of Dean College

LONGMAN

Addison Wesley Longman Limited
Edinburgh Gate, Harlow
Essex CM20 2JE, England
and Associated Companies throughout the world

© Addison Wesley Longman Limited 1997

First published 1997

British Library Cataloguing in Publication Data
A catalogue entry for this title is available from the British Library

ISBN 0-582-30298-6

Set by 24 in Garamond 10/12 and Univers
Printed in Great Britain by Henry Ling Ltd, at the Dorset Press,
Dorchester, Dorset.

Contents

6   Basic engineering materials   109

7   Handling engineering information   127

Appendices

Acknowledgements

The author and publisher are grateful to the following companies for their help during the preparation of this text, and for permission to reproduce copyright materials: L.S. Starrett Company Ltd; Moore & Wright; Rupert & Co. Ltd; WDS Limited.

Chapter 1

General health and safety

Exercise		Page	Date	Signed by Trainer
1.1	Employee's duties under the Health and Safety at Work Act 1974	3		
1.2	Referral to other important industrial regulations	4		
1.3	Identification of warning signs for groups of hazardous substances	5		
1.4	Observation of first aid and accident reporting procedures	8		
1.5	Description of the causes of fire	9		
1.6	Description of fire prevention methods and escape procedure	9		
1.7	Identification of the types and uses of fire extinguishers	10		
1.8	Selection and use of protective clothing and equipment	11		
1.9	Demonstration of the correct technique for manually lifting heavy loads	14		
1.10	Use of safe working practices	14		
1.11	Safe use and storage of tools, equipment and materials	15		
1.12	Recognition and use of various types of guard	17		
1.13	Observation of safety rules, signs and hazard warnings	18		
1.14	Health and safety test	19		
All information presented in this section is complete, accurate and legible				
All information presented in this section is in the format required				
The trainee observes statutory regulations at all times				
The trainee implements safe operating practice and always demonstrates regard for the safety of others				

Health and safety legislation

Health and safety is probably the most important element in the working life of all people. Craft engineers work in an environment which can potentially be very dangerous. Only when dangers are recognised and understood can appropriate measures be taken to protect against personal accidental injury, ill health or damage to equipment.

Over the years, governments have passed safety laws to ensure that both employers and employees observe health and safety measures while at work. The most important of these laws is the Health and Safety at Work Act 1974, which applies to virtually all persons at work in any job whether employers, employees or self-employed. The Act is long and detailed, but the most important sections are outlined below.

The Health and Safety at Work Act 1974 places the responsibility of safe working practices onto all these parties:

- Employers
- Employees and self-employed
- Designers, manufacturers and suppliers of goods and materials

Health and safety inspectors can inspect premises, any breach of the duties in the Act may result in improvement or prohibition notices being served. Sometimes criminal prosecutions may follow.

Employers

The Act states:

It shall be the duty of every employer to ensure, so far as is reasonably practicable, the health, safety and welfare at work of all his employees.

This extends to:

- Providing and maintaining safe plant and systems of work. All machinery and equipment should be safe and in good working order. Protective clothing and appropriate safety equipment should be made available free of charge for employees to use.
- Arranging the safe use, handling, storage and transportation of articles and substances. Transportation includes all cranes, trolleys and appropriate routes to be used.
- Providing information, instruction, training and supervision to ensure the health and safety of all employees. This includes the provision of safety signs and warnings.
- Maintaining a safe place of work, including access and exit routes. Buildings and workplaces must comply with the safety standards and correct emergency procedures implemented.
- Providing and maintaining safe facilities and arrangements for employees' welfare at work, e.g. proper heating and lighting, adequate washrooms and cloakrooms.

Besides any responsibilities towards his or her employees, an employer's duties under the Act apply to subcontractors, visitors and the general public, whose health and safety may be affected by his or her activities (e.g. harmful emissions to the atmosphere or hazards in a reception area).

Employees

Employees are also bound by the requirements of the Health and Safety at Work Act:

It shall be the duty of every employee, whilst at work...

- To take reasonable care for the health and safety of himself and others who may be affected by his actions or omissions.
- To cooperate with his employer so far as is necessary, to enable the employer to carry out his duties.

This means that all employees *must* wear suitable protective clothing provided; use protective equipment and guards provided; maintain their work area in a tidy manner; behave sensibly; apply safe working practices; be familiar with emergency procedures; take notice of warning and information signs; cooperate with supervisors and report all accidents, dangers and incidents. Employees *must not* work on machinery without instruction and supervision nor should they interfere with or misuse anything provided to protect their health, safety or welfare.

Other parties

Designers, manufacturers and suppliers of goods and materials must also comply with the Health and Safety at Work Act, by ensuring all articles designed, made or sold are safe when properly used.

Employees' duties under the Act

During your training there must be a person appointed to supervise you and offer advice and assistance to ensure the safety of yourself and others. The appointed person is called your **supervisor**.

In the event of your supervisor not being available, another person must be delegated and you should be aware of this. The organisation's safety officer or the qualified first aider can also be approached if you need specialist advice and/or assistance.

Exercise 1.1

Employees duties under the Health and Safety at Work Act 1974

Part A

It is your duty to know who the following personnel are and where to find them in your organisation. Complete the table below with the names and the usual location of the named persons.

Position	Name	Location
Your supervisor		
Safety officer		
First aider		

Part B

Considering the notes on the previous page about the Health and Safety at Work Act 1974, write brief comments regarding the employee's (your) duties in the following circumstances:

1. You are not sure how to operate the machine required for the task in hand.

2. You need to carry some sharp metal parts to a storage area.

3. Your machine's guard is broken.

4. You have lost your safety glasses.

5. The machine you are operating has spilt coolant onto the floor.

6. Your supervisor tells you to tidy up a mess that someone else has made.

Other important regulations

The Health and Safety at Work Act 1974 covers virtually everyone in all kinds of work. For more specialist engineering legal information about a process or particular method of protecting an operator, it may be necessary to refer to one or more of the following acts or regulations:

- Grinding Metals Special Regulations 1925 and 1950
- The Factories Act 1961
- The Abrasive Wheel Regulations 1970
- Power Press Regulations 1965 and 1972
- Eyeshield Regulations 1974
- The Electricity at Work Regulations 1989
- COSHH (Control of Substances Harmful to Health) Regulations 1989 and 1994
- Manual Handling Operations Regulations 1992
- Personal Protective Equipment Regulations 1992
- Provision and Use of Work Equipment Regulations 1992

Exercise 1.2 *Referral to other important industrial regulations*

Complete the table by selecting the most relevant regulations from the list above. The milling guards section has been filled in for guidance.

Milling guards	Provision and use of work equipment regulations 1992
	Factories act 1961
Eye protection	
Safe use of power presses	
Safety clothing	
Abrasive wheels	
Electrical switches	

Warning signs for hazardous substances

Exercise 1.3 *Identification of warning signs for groups of hazardous substances*

[See also Exercise 7.2 Handling engineering information]

For each of the hazardous substance warning signs below, state the information that is being given and write an example of what material it might be. The first has been completed for your guidance.

Warning sign	Group of hazardous substances	
	Type of hazard	Flammable material
	Example	Petrol
	Type of hazard	
	Example	
	Type of hazard	
	Example	
	Type of hazard	
	Example	
	Type of hazard	
	Example	
	Type of hazard	
	Example	
	Type of hazard	
	Example	

First aid procedures

Under the Health and Safety (First Aid) Regulations, workplaces must have first aid provision. In general, this includes a suitably trained first aider and at least one adequately stocked first aid box that is clearly labelled. Note that first aid boxes are primarily for the use of the registered first aiders.

It is always best to get a qualified first aider to the scene of the incident as soon as possible. Where possible stay with the casualty and send someone to get the first aider. If for any reason the first aider is not available, dial 999 and ask for an ambulance.

However, it is important to know what to do in the event of the first aider not being immediately available and certainly in the case of electrocution.

Electric shock

If someone gets an **electric shock**, it may be evident from one of the following:

- You hear a shout.
- You hear a bang.
- You notice a flash.
- The electric supply is cut off.

Turning off the power **before** rescuing

Do not touch the casualty until the current is switched off.
On no account should you risk becoming electrocuted.

If the current cannot be switched off, free the casualty from the electrical source with insulating gloves to BS 697 (where available) or with some dry, non-conducting material (e.g. a wooden stick or a wooden chair).

The casualty might be:

- Not breathing
- In a state of shock
- Suffering other injuries
- Burnt
- At risk of collapsing later in the day

You should follow this procedure:

1. Send for the first aider.
2. Start artificial respiration if the casualty is not breathing (see below).
3. Continue until further medical aid arrives.
4. Reassure the casualty that help is on its way.

Allow casualty to rest and keep him or her under observation.

Deep cut

If someone gets a **deep cut**, follow this procedure:

1. Send for the first aider.
2. Wash the cut area in a flow of clean cold water.
3. Hold the injury up high.
4. Wrap or bandage firmly.
5. Rest in a comfortable position until further medical help arrives.
6. Reassure the casualty that help is on its way.

Raise a wound after cleaning it in cold water

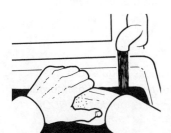

Rinsing chemicals off the affected area with clean cold water.

Cooling a burn with cold water.

Keeping a suspected broken bone still whilst the casualty is kept warm

Chemical burn

If someone gets a **chemical burn**, follow this procedure:

1. Send for the first aider.
2. Remove any contaminated clothing which is not stuck to the skin.
3. Rinse the area thoroughly with flowing clean cold water for 10 to 15 minutes.
4. Keep the affected area clean.
5. Reassure the casualty that help is on its way.

Heat burn

If someone gets a **heat burn**, follow this procedure:

1. Send for the first aider.
2. Rinse the area with flowing clean cold water for 10 minutes (or until the first aider arrives).
3. Keep the burnt area as still as possible.
4. Reassure the casualty that help is on its way.

- **Never** touch the affected area.
- **Never** apply ointments to the affected area.
- **Never** remove clothing.

Broken bone

If you suspect that someone has a **broken bone**, follow this procedure:

1. Send for the first aider.
2. Do *not* move the casualty unless he or she is in a dangerous position.
3. Keep the casualty warm.
4. Reassure the casualty that help is on its way.

Artificial respiration procedure

1. Send for expert help.
2. Remove obstructions from casualty's airway.
3. Raise the nape of the casualty's neck and press his or her forehead back (to straighten the airway).
4. Pinch the casualty's nose and seal your lips round his or her opened mouth.
5. Blow firmly into the casualty's mouth until his or her chest rises.
6. Allow the casualty's chest to fall.

Continue the process about 12 times per minute (every 5 seconds) until expert help arrives.

Nape of the casualty's neck raised and his forehead pressed back.

Blowing into the casualty's mouth with his nose sealed.

Watching his chest fall to its original position.

Accident reporting procedures

Exercise 1.4

Observation of first aid and accident reporting procedures

1. State the location of the first aid box for your work area.

2. Complete the drawing to illustrate the symbol that appears on first aid boxes.

3. State the name of the first aider for your work area and where the first aider is normally located.

4. The Reporting of Injuries, Diseases and Dangerous Occurrences Regulations 1995 (RIDDOR 95) require deaths or major injuries, work-related diseases and dangerous occurrences to be reported. Study the HSE pamphlet *Everyone's guide to RIDDOR*, then answer the following questions:

   (a) Give two examples of major injury.
      (i)

      (ii)

   (b) Give two examples of work-related diseases.
      (i)

      (ii)

   (c) Give two examples of dangerous occurrences.
      (i)

      (ii)

5. State the accident reporting procedure that you should follow if you are involved in an accident.

The causes of fire

Fires can have devastating effects on industrial and domestic premises. After a serious fire, 43 per cent of firms never trade again. Fire strikes in a variety of ways and we all must be aware of how to avoid danger to ourselves and our workmates in the event of a fire. Fires cost lives and jobs.

An outbreak of fire requires the presence of all three of these elements:

- **Fuel** – some material that burns.
- **Heat** – the temperature at which fuels ignite (the flash point) varies from one fuel to another.
- **Oxygen** – present in the air.

If fuel, heat and oxygen are all present a fire could develop. Some common causes of fire in industrial premises are listed below:

- Electrical faults
- Discarded cigarette ends
- Gas and electric welding

Exercise 1.5

Description of the causes of fire

Find out three more possible causes of fire and write them in the space provided.

1.

2.

3.

Fire prevention methods and escape procedure

Fire is a serious risk, so all premises need to have reliable measures to help prevent injury and minimise damage.

Exercise 1.6

Description of fire prevention methods and escape procedure

Part A
Common fire precaution measures are listed below. For each one, find an example in your work area and write its location in the space provided.

- Fire doors

- Fire alarm system

- Fire extinguishers

- Water sprinklers

- Emergency exits

Part B
The evacuation procedure is not only for fires but for any emergency. It should be known to all personnel in the building and must be supported by information notices. The fire procedure should be practised at regular intervals.

Draw a map in the space below of the route you must follow if a fire breaks out in your work area.

Write here the procedure you should follow if a fire breaks out in your workplace. The first item has been completed for your guidance:

1. Sound the fire alarm.

2.

3.

4.

5.

In a practice fire drill it takes .... (time) to get to the assembly point.

The types and uses of fire extinguishers

If a fire is tackled when it is small there is less chance of it getting out of control. This can be done with a portable fire extinguisher. Care must be taken to select and use the appropriate type of extinguisher for the type of fire. It can be dangerous to use an inappropriate extinguisher, particularly if there is an electrical supply in the fire. *When fighting a fire always ensure your escape route is clear.* Fire extinguishers work by preventing the oxygen from reaching the flames or by removing the heat from the fuel; some types of fire extinguisher work in both ways. The most common types of fire extinguisher are listed below, together with the types of fire for which they are most suitable.

| **Exercise 1.7** | *Identification of the types and uses of fire extinguishers* |

Locate all the types of fire extinguisher in your workplace and record their colours in the table. Read the instructions regarding how to operate each type and also add a note to describe the correct methods of operation.

Type	Colour	Uses and method of operation
Water		**Used on solid fuelled fires, not electrical apparatus** To operate:
Foam		**Used on liquid and solid fuelled fires** To operate:
Dry powder		**Used on liquid, solid and electrically fuelled fires** To operate:
Carbon dioxide		**Used on liquid and electrically fuelled fires** To operate:

Protective clothing and equipment

Exercise 1.8 *Selection and use of protective clothing and equipment*

In each of the following three sections, complete the blank spaces as instructed

Protective clothing
This drawing shows an engineering trainee dressed in a potentially dangerous way. List ten points that are a potential hazard to his safety.

1. His long hair is not contained	**6.**	
2.	**7.**	
3.	**8.**	
4.	**9.**	
5.	**10.**	

Safety boots

A pair of safety boots made to BS 1870 will have many safety features. The most noticeable feature is steel toecaps. These can protect the toes should a heavy object be dropped onto the foot. Other safety features on some industrial footwear are listed below. Add to the table a short note to indicate the circumstances when the feature is required.

Non-slip rubber sole	Chemical-resistant soles	
Ankle protection	Oil-resistant soles	
Steel inner of sole	Quick-release laces	

Work environment

Briefly explain the work environment that would require the following safety clothing and equipment, and state why they are necessary. The first one has been completed for your guidance.

1. Overalls

   Overalls are necessary when there are moving parts of machinery and the engineer needs to keep his or her loose clothing contained to prevent entanglement.

2. Safety glasses

3. Helmet

4. Safety boots

5. Hats

6. Ear protectors

7. Aprons

8. Barrier cream

9. Three different types of gloves

   (a) Leather

   (b) Asbestos (substitute)

   (c) Rubber

10. When carrying out work where pieces of material might fly about, e.g. chiselling, it may be necessary to erect a screen to protect others working nearby or passing your work area. Find such a screen in your workplace and sketch it below.

Lifting and carrying techniques

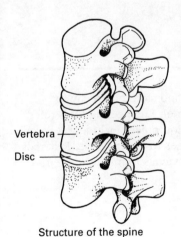

Vertebra

Disc

Structure of the spine

The human spine is a column of cylindrical bones called **vertebrae**. The column is held together by string ligaments, and each vertebra is separated by a disc. The disc material is flexible so that movement is possible, and also allows shocks to be absorbed. If the spine is strained while lifting or carrying, the ligaments can be damaged or the discs may be displaced. These injuries are acutely painful. For engineers the most common cause of back trouble is poor lifting technique, so it is important to understand how to lift safely. For the back to be at its strongest, the spine should be vertical. Hence, when lifting heavy or awkward loads, you should bend at the knees and keep your head up rather than bending the back.

WRONG
Back bent and head down

RIGHT
Bending at the knees, head kept well up

Never attempt to lift more than 20 kg without assistance. Always ask for help with bulky loads and ensure that any load being transported does not obstruct your vision. If assistance is not available, use powered lifting equipment. Remember it is good practice to clear the area you are going to put the load on *before* it is picked up.

| Exercise 1.9 | *Demonstration of the correct technique for manually lifting heavy loads* |

Demonstrate to your assessor the correct technique for manually lifting a heavy load. Identify the alternative means of lifting or moving a load that are available to you if the load is too heavy or bulky for you to handle alone.

Signed satisfactory by supervisor..

Safe working practices

| Exercise 1.10 | *Use of safe working practices* |

Give three reasons why it is always necessary to maintain the work area, exits and gangways in a clean and tidy condition to conform with the Health and Safety at Work Act 1974.

1.

2.

3.

This trainee keeps the work area clean and tidy

Signed satisfactory by supervisor..

Use and storage of items

Engineering tools and equipment should always be used and stored correctly to minimise accidents and to keep them in good working order. Engineering tools refer to hand tools, measuring tools and powered hand tools. Equipment includes all types of equipment used in the workshop from vices and benches to lifting tackle. Materials should be stored and transported carefully and in such a way as to minimise the risk of injury.

Safe use of tools and equipment

- Carefully select the correct tool for the job.
- Never use any tools/equipment without full instruction or training. If you're not sure, ask your supervisor.
- Check tools/equipment for any obvious faults, damage or excessive wear before use. Never use a faulty tool or equipment, report it to your supervisor.
- Always follow set safety rules and procedures, e.g. files must be fitted with handles, guards used on machine tools, protective clothing worn when necessary.
- For powered hand tools, use 110 V equipment with a transformer whenever possible, the lower voltage significantly reduces the severity of electric shocks.
- Know the emergency stop procedures for all powered tools and machines.
- Take care when laying power-tool cords; avoid 'trip wires'.
- Switch off the electrical supply after working electrical hand tools.

- Never work electrically powered hand tools with wet hands, near water or flammable liquids.
- Treat all tools/equipment with respect and never use any tools or operate machinery if you are unwell or unfit to do so.

Safe storage of tools and equipment

- All tools and equipment must be stored in a way that does not present a risk of injury to persons, e.g. sharp edges should be covered, long items should not protrude from shelves.
- After use, tools and equipment should be cleaned as instructed.
- Tools and equipment should be tidily stored in a clean and dry place.
- Tools and equipment should be stored in their specially allocated place to enable easy retrieval. If issued by the stores they should be returned there.
- Accurate measuring tools may be lightly oiled before being stored to prevent corrosion.

Safe handling and storage of materials

- Always use correct lifting techniques.
- Wear appropriate protective clothing to guard against possible injury.
- Store materials away from gangways.
- Keep naked flames away from flammable materials.
- Liquids should be moved only in sealed containers to avoid splashing.
- Gas cylinders should be kept in well-ventilated areas and away from risk of impact.
- Hot materials should cool down in protected areas.
- Observe and obey any special instructions or safety signs.

Exercise 1.11   *Safe use and storage of tools, equipment and materials*

Part A

Study a selection of hand tools, measuring tools and materials you use on a regular basis, and complete the table below. The first row is completed for your guidance.

Tool	Safety handling precautions while in use	Guards or equipment required
Hand tool e.g. Hammer	Ensure handle is free from oil and grease. Hold tightly at end of shaft	Wear safety glasses
Hand tool e.g.		
Measuring tool e.g.		
Equipment e.g.		
Material e.g.		

Part B

Note the storage system for each of the items you have listed above. Are they stored safely? Complete the safety checklist below. The first one is completed for your guidance.

Tool	Where stored	Kept in case	Check on condition
Hand tool e.g. Hammer	Tool rack.	No	Head is secure Shaft not split
Hand tool e.g.			
Measuring tool e.g.			
Equipment e.g.			
Material e.g.			
To whom are defects reported?			

Recognition and use of guards

The purpose of a guard is to protect. Guards may be designed to protect people, fragile workpieces or machine parts. There are many types of guard used in engineering today. Some of the purposes of guards are listed below. Note that guards have many methods of operation. Most guards are mechanical barriers and may be transparent. Some guards are electrical and operate either as 'magic eyes' to switch off a machine if an invisible beam is broken, or as interlocks to prevent a machine from working until it is safe.

Guards may be used to:

- Protect operators, and others who may be passing, from getting into contact with moving parts.
- Prevent swarf and other particles flying out of machines and causing injuries.
- Prevent objects coming into contact with items of machinery which may be delicate or fragile.
- Prevent unauthorised persons working machines.
- Keep people or their limbs out of danger areas.
- Prevent a machine damaging itself.

| **Exercise 1.12** | *Recognition and use of various types of guard* |

For each of the spaces provided sketch an appropriate guard and state how it works.

1. Guard to protect hands

2. Guard to protect eyes

3. Guard to protect equipment

4. Guard to protect persons from moving parts

5. Electronic 'interlock' switch

This trainee always uses appropriate safety precautions to the task being undertaken

Signed satisfactory by supervisor...

Safety rules and hazard warnings

Employers put up various signs in order to ensure that employees are aware of the dangers in work areas and of the precautions necessary to reduce risk. The five categories of sign described below are the recommended shape and colour to meet with page 6 of the Safety Signs at Work Regulations.

Exercise 1.13 *Observation of safety rules, signs and hazard warnings*

Complete column 1 by drawing the correct sign; complete column 2 by writing the meaning of each sign in the space. The mandatory signs are shown completed for your guidance.

Category	Column 1	Column 2
1 Mandatory (compulsory) White picture or image on a round blue background	Safety boots must be worn	*You must wear safety glasses*
2 Prohibition (forbidden) Black picture on a round white background surrounded by a red border and diagonal line	Do not drink this water	
3 Danger Warning Black picture on a yellow background with triangular black edging	Warning of high voltages	
4 Emergency information White picture or words on a green background, rectangular in shape	Fire assembly point	EXIT
5 Fire information White picture or words on a red background, rectangular in shape	Fire extinguisher point	

This trainee keeps the work area clean and tidy

Signed satisfactory by supervisor...

Exercise 1.14   *Health and safety test*

The multiple choice question paper will only be issued to candidates by their supervisor on satisfactory completion of the appropriate exercises. The answer sheet below must be completed by the candidate when the questions are issued.

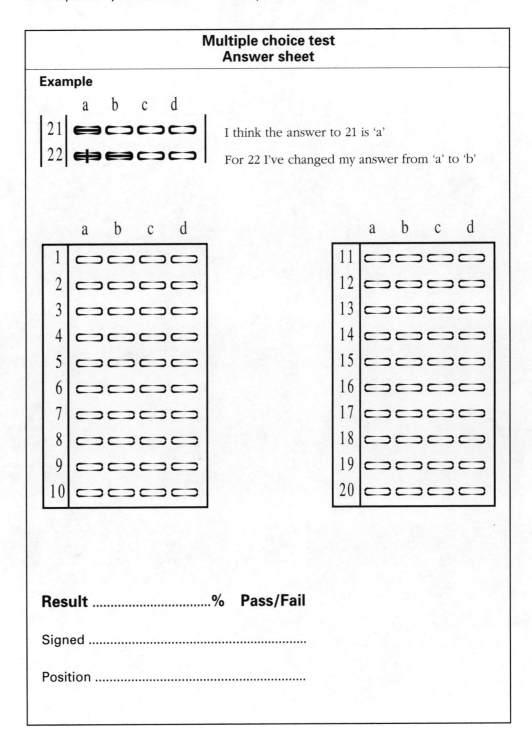

**Multiple choice test
Answer sheet**

Example

21   I think the answer to 21 is 'a'

22   For 22 I've changed my answer from 'a' to 'b'

Result ....% **Pass/Fail**

Signed ....

Position ....

Chapter 2
Establishing effective working relationships

Exercise		Page	Date	Signed by Trainer
2.1	Dress, presentation and behaviour	23		
2.2	Handling instructions effectively	25		
2.3	Seeking help from appropriate persons when necessary	26		
2.4	Asking for and giving help in an appropriate manner	28		
2.5	Reporting deficiencies in tools, equipment and materials	29		
2.6	Respecting the property and views of others	30		
2.7	Integration and cooperation: company organisation chart	31		
2.8	Reporting difficulties in working relationships	32		
2.9	Establishing effective working relationships test	33		
All information presented in this section is complete, accurate and legible				
All information presented in this section is in the format required				

Good working relationships are an important part of the working lives of everyone. People should be able to get on with each other and work well as a group or team to achieve the best results for their organisation and the welfare of its staff. If working relationships are good, the workforce becomes effective and efficient, and working relationships improve even further.

This chapter will assist you to understand and develop the personal skills necessary for effective working relationships. These personal skills should be integrated and continued throughout your NVQ training and you should not view this chapter in isolation or as a free-standing unit.

The exercises require you to give evidence in the form of examples of situations during your training where you have demonstrated the relevant skill. Your evidence will therefore relate to the work you have done at any time during your training and there may be some cross-referencing with other chapters.

The exercises need not be completed in the order in which they appear. For example, you may decide to start with *Exercise 2.3*; for example:

Exercise 2.3	*Seeking help from appropriate persons when necessary*
	When you feel that you've been asking for help from the appropriate people, complete the exercise below, then ask your supervisor to sign relevant section.

Trainee's evidence

Describe a situation where you asked a colleague for practical assistance

When I had to move a heavy surface plate I asked J. Smith to give me a hand.

Describe a situation where you asked your supervisor for advice about safe working practices.

I asked the Supervisor to advise me about how to sharpen the scriber's point safely.

Describe a situation where you were directed to another person for help

When doing the organisation chart (Exercise 2.7) I asked the Supervisor to help me, he told me to go to reception and ask the secretary.

Supervisor's confirmation

Confirmation by supervisor that the trainee asks the appropriate person for help when necessary

Signed by supervisor ......*A. Supervisor*..............

Dress, presentation and behaviour

Dress and presentation

Being correctly dressed and well presented can positively influence your performance at work, your safety and how other people see you.

If you are clean, tidily dressed and well presented you will feel better in yourself and more able to work effectively. Being correctly dressed means wearing clothes appropriate for the work; clothes should be practical, protective, safe and give some indication of your role.

In the engineering workshop appropriate clothing refers to special protective clothing, usually overalls, eye protection and safety footwear. Under the Health and Safety at Work Act 1974 it is the law that appropriate safety clothing must be worn in engineering workshops (see Chapter 1).

Staff employed in other areas would also be expected to dress appropriately, e.g. a receptionist should always dress smartly and a director may wear a suit, a storekeeper will usually wear a dustcoat.

Being well presented isn't only about your appearance, it is also evident in your manner such as speaking clearly, being positive and showing interest.

Behaviour in the workplace

Good behaviour and a positive attitude to work are necessary aspects of working life to maintain good working relations. By behaving in a sensible way you are likely to gain the confidence and trust of others and are unlikely to offend colleagues.

In a potentially dangerous environment such as an engineering workshop, good behaviour, following the rules and obeying your supervisor are vitally important to avoiding accidents. Accidents don't just happen, they are caused. Make sure your behaviour is never the cause of an accident. It is the law under the Health and Safety at Work Act that an employee must '*take reasonable care of himself and other persons who may be affected by his actions and omissions at work,*' i.e. what an employee does, or should have done (see Chapter 1).

Most companies and training organisations have in-house rules to specify behaviour that is acceptable/unacceptable in the workshops and other areas. The *common* behaviour rules are tabulated below.

Always	Never
Dress appropriately.	Operate machines without guards.
Seek advice when unsure how to proceed.	Distract others operating machines.
Know emergency procedures.	Run in the workshop.
Obey rules and safety signs.	Leave a machine running unattended.
Stack materials carefully.	Smoke in prohibited areas.
Keep gangways clear.	Play with compressed air lines.
Keep the work area clean and tidy.	Throw anything.

Good behaviour and a positive attitude often go hand in hand. Someone who is well behaved, trustworthy, cooperative, respectful and tries hard is said to have a **positive** or good attitude. It's always best to begin with and maintain a positive attitude at work; colleagues and supervisors will notice and be much more cooperative and willing to see you do well.

Exercise 2.1 | *Dress, presentation and behaviour*

When you consider that your dress, presentation and behaviour have been constantly appropriate for your workplace, and within the scope of the Health and Safety at Work Act, complete the exercise below and ask your supervisor to sign the relevant section.

Trainee's evidence

Describe the appropriate clothing you wear which is required for your workplace

Describe a situation where you needed to use special safety equipment

Supervisor's confirmation

Confirmation by supervisor that your dress, presentation and behaviour is appropriate for the workplace

Signed by supervisor ....

Instructions

The smooth running of any company depends on the employees carrying out instructions properly and promptly. Instructions can be handed down through a management structure and given to the person who is best suited to undertaking the task. A chart showing the organisation of a typical engineering company is illustrated below.

Whenever an instruction is issued to you by your supervisor you should act on it promptly. But if you are busy carrying out the previous task, you would normally finish that first unless your supervisor tells you otherwise.

You should cooperate with your supervisor by doing what he or she says, but remember to communicate any queries you may have or any information you think he or she should know. For example, if your supervisor has given you an instruction to do a task at the same time as you are due to sit your exams, you must explain this.

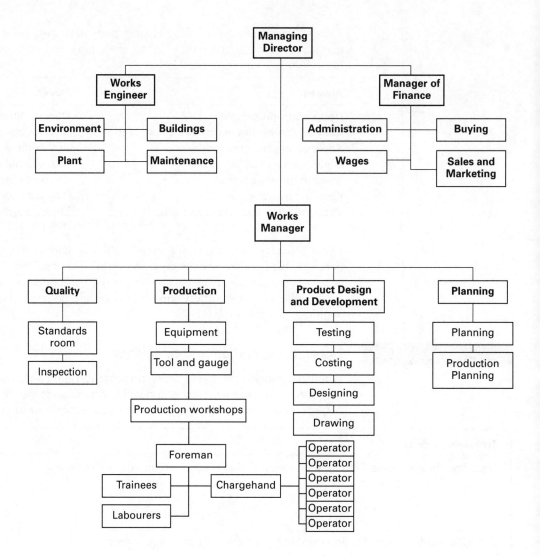

Once your supervisor knows you will be unavailable, he or she can arrange for someone else to do the task if necessary.

You must be clear about instructions issued to you before you act upon them. Otherwise accidents and unnecessary expense may be caused by incorrect use of machines, selection of the wrong materials or tools, and time wasted by having to do the work all over again. There are several types of instructions:

- **Verbal instructions** – given by your supervisor; verbal instructions should be summarised and repeated back. By doing this you are clarifying what needs to be done and your supervisor then knows that you understand the instructions. If you haven't quite heard, remembered or understood the instruction, ask the supervisor to go through it with you again.
- **Written instructions/drawings** – sometimes unclear, written instructions may not always be legible or the information on a drawing may appear to be missing. Instructions are sometimes presented in an unfamiliar format. If you are unsure of any aspect, ask your supervisor to clarify it.

When in doubt about instructions, ask!

Once you have understood the instruction, you need to act upon it. Any instruction to do anything should be done according to the correct procedures, accurately and with as much care as possible. Take pride in your work. Concentrate and plan the task in hand, double-check your planning, double-check your work.

| Exercise 2.2 | *Handling instructions effectively* |

When you consider you can handle instructions effectively, complete the exercise below and ask your supervisor to sign the relevant section.

Trainee's evidence

Describe a situation where you sought clarification of instructions then executed them accurately and promptly

---

Supervisor's confirmation

Confirmation by your supervisor that you seek clarification and confirmation of instructions before starting work

Signed by supervisor ....

Confirmation by your supervisor that you carry out instructions cooperatively and accurately.

Signed by supervisor ....

Asking for help and giving help

Help may be advice on how to perform a task, it may be practical assistance with a task, or it may even be both. Sometimes you know what needs to be done, but you don't know how to do it, maybe through a lack of knowledge or experience on your part. This is a common occurrence and you should ask for advice after having first tried to work things out yourself.

Sometimes you may know what needs to be done and how to do it but you need practical assistance, then you will need to ask someone.

> **Never** *be afraid to ask for help.*
> **Never** *be afraid to ask again if you still need to.*

Who should you ask?

Your supervisor has a responsibility to look after you, so you should generally ask your supervisor. However, there are others you could ask, e.g. experienced colleagues, other personnel, or an experienced person arranged by your supervisor. Whoever you ask, remember to cooperate with them as much as possible.

- **Colleagues** – often pleased to help along with other more experienced staff. They can offer practical assistance and provide you with general day-to-day information. A colleague can be asked if you need help with:

  (a) Information   e.g. the location of a certain book, reference table or manual

  (b) Advice   e.g. how to use conversion tables

  (c) Practical assistance e.g. holding tape in position while you measure the length of something

- **Supervisor** – you are directly responsible to your supervisor, you must check work procedures with him or her. Never be afraid to ask the supervisor. A supervisor would normally be able to help in these situations:

  (a) Clarification

  e.g. clarification of instructions or unclear advice from a colleague

  (b) Reassurance and guidance:

  e.g. if you are unsure about the exact fitting of a machine guard

  (c) Safety

  e.g. if you are uncertain about the safety aspects of *anything*

  (d) Methods of working

  e.g. if you are unsure about the operation of a machine, *never* proceed until you have asked and been shown, either by the supervisor or by a nominated instructor

- **Other personnel** – your supervisor may refer you to other personnel for advice and assistance; among others, it could be:

  (a) Safety officer

  e.g. safety aspects of materials not normally used in the workshop like spray paint

  (b) Clerical assistant

  e.g. filling in forms and replying to letters

  (c) First aider

  e.g. for reporting injuries and accidents

  (d) Union official

  e.g. affairs which are beyond the normal scope of the supervisor

  (e) Counsellor

  e.g. if you have a personal problem

  (f) Manager

  e.g. for commendations or discipline

| Exercise 2.3 | *Seeking help from appropriate persons when necessary* |

When you feel that you've been asking for help from the appropriate people, complete the exercise below then ask your supervisor to sign the relevant section.

Trainee's evidence
Describe a situation where you asked a colleague for practical assistance
Describe a situation where you asked your supervisor for advice about safe working practices
Describe a situation where you were directed to another person for help
Supervisor's comments
Confirmation by supervisor that the trainee asks the appropriate person for help when necessary

Signed by supervisor ....

Asking for help correctly

If you need to ask anyone for help, it is a good idea to consider the manner in which you do so. Consider the time, what they are doing and the manner in which you speak to them. It is quite possible that you may not get the best response from the person you have asked if you don't.

Different people respond well to different approaches, but in general, before asking for help:

- Always try to solve your problem yourself before you ask anyone.
- Try to select a convenient time for the person you're going to ask; if the person you want to ask is continually busy, say 'When you have a moment, please could you show me how to...'
- Try to ask a person who probably knows the information you require.
- Unless it's urgent, don't interrupt the conversation of others.
- Be polite and patient.
- Use good language and avoid offending the person you're asking.
- Don't be a know-all when someone is trying to help you.

Ignore this checklist if there is an urgent safety issue; you must get *immediate* help (see Chapter 1).

Some examples of good manners when asking for help are tabulated below.

Well-mannered approach	ill-mannered approach
Excuse me, please would you explain this again.	Haven't got a clue how to do this, tell me again!
Please would you tell me how to find the tapping size for an M8 × 1.25 thread.	What's the tapping size for this lot?
Is anyone else cold?	I'm too cold, turn the heating on.
Can I do anything to help you?	You're taking ages to do that!

Giving help when asked

Just as you ask your colleagues for help, they may ask you for help. Being part of a team, you should be in a position to discuss what they want, and if you cannot offer help you may be able to suggest an alternative source. Your cooperation will probably be appreciated and they may be more inclined to help you in the future.

But remember:

- Make sure the help you offer is correct and the person understands your answer.
- If you are asked to help with a practical task, listen and do as you are asked.
- If in any doubt about safety issues, and to be absolutely sure, ask the supervisor.
- If you can't help or don't know the answer, say so.
- Never leave a machine running unattended.

But if you are busy with your own work, do not continually go to colleagues' assistance for matters which could wait; otherwise you could jeopardise your own work schedules. If you are busy you could arrange a time to look at a colleague's problem, say in five minutes, or you could suggest someone else who would be suitable.

Exercise 2.4	*Asking for and giving help in an appropriate manner*

When you feel you've been asking for and giving help in the appropriate manner, complete the exercise below and ask your supervisor to sign the relevant section.

Trainee's evidence.

Describe an occasion when you gave help to a colleague

Describe an occasion when you needed to seek help from a colleague

---

Supervisor's confirmation

Confirmation by supervisor that the trainee asks for and gives help to colleagues in an appropriate manner

Signed by supervisor ....

Reporting deficiencies in items

Tools

Tools should always be in good order and must be taken care of properly (see Chapters 4 and 5).

Large organisations may have a regular in-house system for inspecting and calibrating the accuracy of measuring tools in a special area called the standards room. However, many companies send their measuring tools away for inspection and calibration.

Many organisations have a set procedure for reporting inaccurate tools. If this is the case and you suspect a tool is defective, you should follow the set procedure. If there is no set procedure for reporting a defective tool, the supervisor must be contacted and informed.

Equipment

If you are working on a job and the equipment you are using no longer works as you would expect, do not attempt to repair it. If the equipment is a machine, switch it off and immediately report it to the supervisor with all the information about the problem. The supervisor will then take the appropriate action. This may be advice to you regarding the correct operation of the equipment if you have been using it incorrectly, or contacting the maintenance department for repair if there is a fault.

Materials

Material defects are described in detail in Chapter 6. The defects may not only be within the materials, e.g. a blowhole in a casting, but it could be that the size or shape of the material with which you are issued is not suited to your task.

Exercise 2.5	*Reporting deficiencies in tools, equipment and materials*

When you know the procedure for reporting defective tools, equipment and materials, complete the exercise below and ask your supervisor to sign the relevant section.

Trainee's evidence
Describe the set procedures for reporting defective tools, equipment and materials
Briefly describe an occasion when you correctly reported a suspected deficiency in a measuring tool, some marking-out equipment or a material.
Supervisor's confirmation
Confirmation that the trainee is familiar with and reports all suspected deficiencies in tools, equipment and materials according to the set procedures
Signed by supervisor ....

Respect for others

Respecting the views of others

You can choose your friends but not your colleagues (or relatives). Considering you have to work with colleagues, it makes sense to try to get on with them as well as possible and to respect their views and values on work and life, which may be different to your own. Sometimes you may not agree with what is being said; certainly people do not all think in the same way. However, by recognising people's differences, you should be able to put them aside and work together as best you can.

At work there are usually set procedures, but sometimes part of a job may be open to interpretation. If you disagree with a colleague's interpretation and method, there is no point in jumping in and arguing about it, listen to their views and consider carefully. Ask your supervisor for advice if there is still uncertainty.

Remember that those in charge have been appointed to their position on merit and are usually experienced. Pay attention to your supervisor and other personnel in senior positions then follow their advice.

Respecting the property of others

If you need to borrow tools or equipment from a workmate, it is important to ask properly, to look after them appropriately and to return them promptly in the condition you received them. This contributes to good teamwork. If you breach this protocol, you may lose the trust of your workmates and they may feel less inclined to lend items to you again.

The tools used from the company or college store should also be looked after properly. Most storekeepers will treat the tools and equipment in their store as their own and have pride in keeping them in good order. If you treat the equipment issued with care and respect, the storekeeper should be helpful to you and issue you with the best equipment at his or her disposal.

| **Exercise 2.6** | *Respecting the property and views of others* |

When you consider you have shown respect for people and their property, complete the exercise below and ask your supervisor to complete the relevant section.

Trainee's evidence
Describe a situation where you regularly borrow and return tools and equipment correctly

Supervisor's confirmation
Confirmation by supervisor that the trainee respects the property and views of others
Signed by supervisor ....

Teamwork, cooperation and integration

At work it may be that much of your time will be spent working as an individual under supervision, or working constantly alongside colleagues. Whatever the situation, you, your colleagues and your supervisor are all members of a working group or team.

Members of any team work well together to achieve the same aims. The aim of a football team should be to score goals by skilful interactive play. At work the aims of engineering team members should be the success of the organisation and the wellbeing of the employees.

Two important aspects of working well in a team or group are cooperation and integration. Throughout this chapter the importance of cooperating with others has been emphasised.

- Cooperation with supervisors when instructions are issued.
- Cooperation with colleagues when help and assistance is required.

Cooperation should also be extended to other individual team members or other teams of workers in the same organisation. For example, if you are working in an engineering drawing office, you should show cooperation, not only to those around you in the drawing office, but to the craftspersons who will have to work from your drawings. Therefore, on a particularly difficult component, you would be cooperating with the craftspersons by adding some extra notes or helpful details to a drawing.

In order to be cooperative to staff outside your immediate area, it is necessary to have some understanding of their work. You cannot cooperate with the craftspersons if you don't know what they do.

In order to have a greater understanding of other workers and working teams, some organisations' trainees undertake work experience in various departments, giving them a better insight into other people's duties and responsibilities.

People working together as part of a team must integrate and relate well to each other. You don't have to be friends with everyone, it isn't human nature. However, you should try to see the best in people and attempt to fit in and work with them as well as you can, so everyone's effort is concentrated on the work and a more pleasant environment is created. Organisations should have positive leadership to encourage the workforce to pull together as a team. This does involve a great deal of trust and respect for each other and people need to feel that their colleagues are working hard and doing their bit. An example of integrated teamwork at college would be working together to leave the workshop neat and tidy for the next working group.

In any organisation there will be people with strengths and weaknesses. The work given to each person should reflect their strong points. Peoples weaknesses should be acknowledged, understood and helped so they are given confidence and not made to feel inferior. For example, someone who has difficulty lifting heavy objects, owing to a weak or injured back, would need a team of helpers to offer help when necessary.

Exercise 2.7 *Integration and cooperation: company organisation chart*

Draw a company organisation chart for your workplace. If your organisation is large, limit the chart to a particular department that is relevant to your training. Include the name of at least one person at each level on the chart and refer to page 24 for a typical company organisation chart.

You will need to research this information by talking to and cooperating with personnel from other sections of the company.

Organisation chart

Confirmation that the trainee has integrated and cooperated with his or her working group and other employees in the organisation

Signed by supervisor ....

Reporting difficulties in working relationships

The majority of people realise the importance of good working relations and will try to get on with others as best they can. However, in working environments, even though there are good working relations, problems among people sometimes arise.

Problem	Example cause
Inconsideration	Ignoring other peoples feelings and needs
Clash of personalities	Difficulties or differences, sometimes related to jealousy
Unfair treatment	Treating people in an unacceptable or unfair way
Lack of trust	Arising from a lack of respect for people and property
Rejection	Deliberately or inadvertently leaving people out
Harassment	Picking on someone or continual sarcasm

In most cases the problems are minor and, with a bit of give and take, they can usually be resolved by discussion among the persons involved. Colleagues who may have noticed a problem – perhaps a workmate is subjected to sarcastic joking – will often step in to help, again by discussion with the persons involved.

It is best to try sorting out any problems there and then, by discussion. However, if this approach has failed or if it is not practical for some reason, it is important that difficulties among colleagues are reported.

In many organisations there are set procedures for reporting problems; the procedures involve some or all of the following persons:

- Supervisor
- Safety representative
- Personnel officer
- Department manager
- Organisation counsellor

All these people have an interest in maintaining good working relations both at work and elsewhere; they should be able to help you.

Exercise 2.8 | *Reporting difficulties in working relationships*

When you know how to report difficulties in working relationships, complete the exercise below and ask your supervisor to complete the relevant section.

Trainee's evidence

Who in your organisation deals with any difficulties you have in your working relationships?

Person/position.

Supervisor's confirmation

Observation by supervisor to confirm the trainee knows the procedure for reporting difficulties in a working relationship

Signed by supervisor ....

Exercise 2.9

Establishing effective working relationships test

The multiple choice question paper will only be issued to candidates by their supervisor on satisfactory completion of the appropriate exercises. The answer sheet below must be completed by the candidate when the questions are issued.

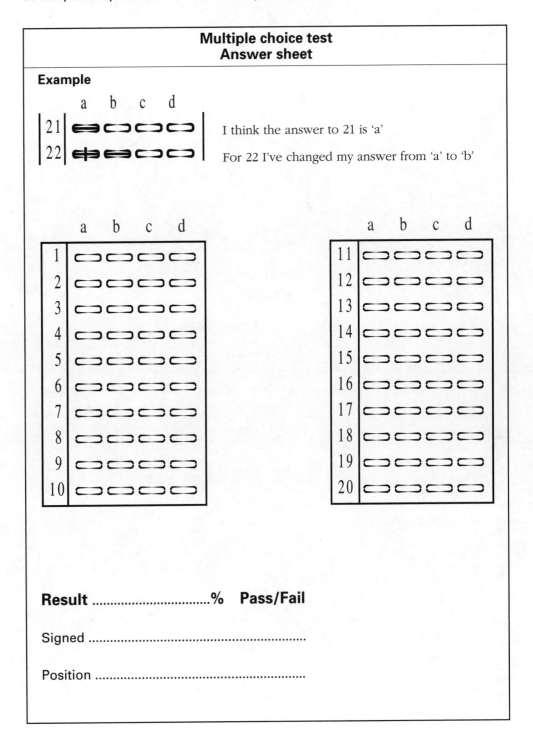

Multiple choice test
Answer sheet

Example

21 I think the answer to 21 is 'a'

22 For 22 I've changed my answer from 'a' to 'b'

Result ....% **Pass/Fail**

Signed ....

Position ....

Chapter 3
Basic engineering drawing

The most effective way of communicating the size, shape and details of a component is to produce an accurate drawing. Drawings are produced by draughtspersons and are used for the costing, planning, manufacture and sale of components. All the features of a component should be clearly shown on a drawing. Drawings should conform to set standards so they can be read by any engineer worldwide. There are several guidelines for engineering drawing layout, forms of projection, types of line, dimensioning methods and symbols. These guidelines are published in a three-part British Standard document known as **BS 308: Engineering Drawing Practice**. The three parts of BS 308 are:

Part 1 – General principles
Part 2 – Dimensioning and tolerancing of size
Part 3 – Geometric tolerancing

This chapter introduces the basics of engineering drawing practice, general principles, dimensioning and tolerancing of size. You will need to refer to BS 308 : Parts 1 and 2 to enable you to complete some of the exercises in accordance with the British Standard guidelines. This chapter also contains an introduction to isometric projection.

Paper sizes

All engineering drawings are printed on paper. The size of the paper mainly depends on the size and scale of the component. The metric A series of paper is normally used as it is standard throughout Europe and most of the world. The actual sheet sizes (in millimetres) are as follows:

- A0 841 × 1189 (1 m²)
- A1 594 × 841
- A2 420 × 594
- A3 297 × 420
- A4 210 × 297

Note that each sheet size is half the previous one.

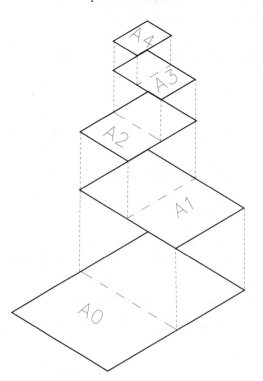

Title block

The paper on which engineering drawings are produced is normally surrounded by a bold border called a **frame**. At the lower right-hand corner of the frame there should be a **title block**; the title block must contain a minimum of six items in order to confirm to BS 308 guidelines:

- Draughtsperson's name or initials (DRAWN)
- Date of drawing
- Projection symbol
- Scale ratio
- Component title
- Drawing number

Further information is nearly always required. A typical blank drawing-page layout is illustrated below.

WHEN IN DOUBT — ASK		PROJECTION		SCALE	DATE
SURFACE FINISH ∇ μm					
DRAWN	UNITS	LIMITS		MATERIAL	
TITLE				NUMBER	

Verification of drawings

It is good practice to check that any drawing being used is current. Engineering drawings are often altered to update specifications, standards and sizes. It is important to ensure the drawing being used is the most recent issue for all work. This verification should be carried out if there are any doubts at all about the correctness of the drawing or its content.

Methods of verifying engineering drawings

- Check the date of issue on the drawing.
- See if there is an expiry date.
- Ask your supervisor if you have any doubts.
- Contact the draughtsperson (where possible) if any doubt persists.

Types of line

Various features on engineering drawings are represented by particular types of line. The table below shows the correct type of line for several applications as recommended in BS 308. The correct type of line should always be used.

Line	Description	Application	Key
————	Continuous bold	Visible outlines	a
		Visible edges	b
————	Continuous fine	Dimension lines	c
		Leader lines	d
		Projection lines	e
		Hatching	f
		Adjacent part outlines	*
∿∿∿	Continuous fine, irregular	Limit of partial view	g
------------	Fine short dashes	Hidden edges	h
		Hidden outlines	*
—·—·—·—	Fine chain	Centre lines	i
▬—·—·—▬	Fine chain, bold at ends and changes of direction	Cutting planes	j

* Not illustrated in Exercise 3.1.

Exercise 3.1

Identification of BS types of line

This drawing of a depth-gauge body illustrates the most common types of line. Complete the labelling by inserting the correct key letter from the above table into the appropriate arrowed circle.

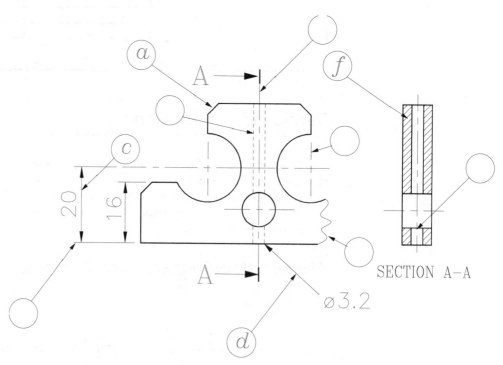

Orthographic projection

Designers need to represent components clearly on paper in the form of drawings if they are to be manufactured as required. The preferred methods of drawing components for manufacture is to set out two or more views of them on paper in a logical manner using a drawing system called orthographic projection. There are two types of orthographic projection; first-angle orthographic projection (first-angle projection) and third-angle orthographic projection (third-angle projection).

First-angle projection

First-angle projection (English projection) is constructed by looking at the component and selecting the faces which reveal the most features. Consider the corner plate shown here. It could be viewed in any of the six planes shown.

VIEWS

A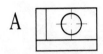

B

C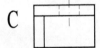

D

E

F

CORNER PLATE

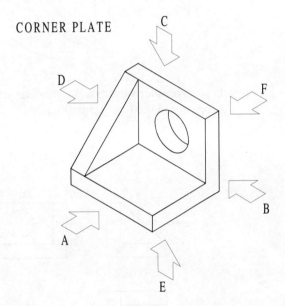

Examination reveals that views A, B and C show the greatest number of visible edges whereas views D, E and F leave some of the details obscured. Three views are generally chosen and the preferred views A, B and C have been selected here as the most appropriate for a first-angle projection of the corner plate.

For the correct layout of the corner plate in **first-angle projection**, the procedure is as follows:

1. The elevation considered to reveal the most features is drawn. For the purpose of this exercise, view A is chosen.

View A

2. View B is then drawn to the **left** of view A. Note that view B is drawn **opposite** the side from which it is viewed (arrow B).

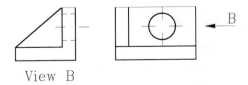

View B

3. View C is drawn directly **below** view A. Note that view C is drawn **opposite** the side from which it is viewed (arrow C).

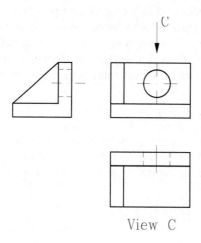

View C

If you consider view B to be the face with the most detail, then the first-angle projection would be drawn like this:

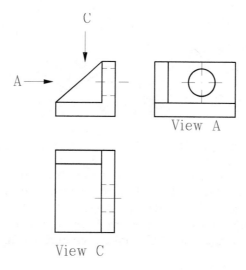

View A

View C

The British Standard symbol for first-angle projection is shown below. This symbol must be included in the title block whenever first-angle projection is used.

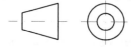

Third-angle projection

Third-angle projection (American projection) is an alternative method of laying out the individual views on the page. When using third-angle projection we use the same planes of projection as described for first-angle projection, but the views are now laid out on the same side as they are viewed from. A drawing of the corner plate in third-angle projection is constructed as follows:

1. The elevation considered to reveal the most features is drawn. For the purpose of this exercise, view A is chosen.

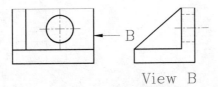

View A

2. View B is now drawn on the **right** of view A. Note that view B is drawn **on** the side from which it is viewed (arrow B).

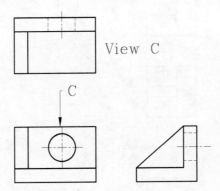

View B

3. View C is drawn directly **above** view A. Note that view C is drawn **on** the side from which it is viewed (arrow C).

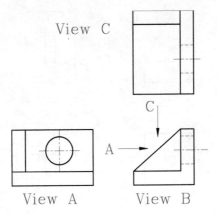

View C

If you consider view B to have the most detail, then the third-angle projection of the corner plate would be laid out like this:

View C

View A   View B

The British Standard symbol for third-angle projection is shown below. This symbol must be included in the title block whenever third-angle projection is used.

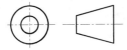

Exercise 3.2 | *Identification of first- and third-angle projection from samples*

Examine carefully the eight orthographic drawings of the angle plate. The drawings are shown in either first- or third-angle projection. Some are drawn wrongly.

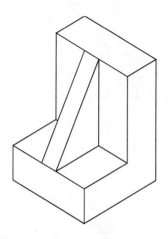

Write in the small box:

1 if first-angle projection is used

3 if third-angle projection is used

X if it is drawn wrongly

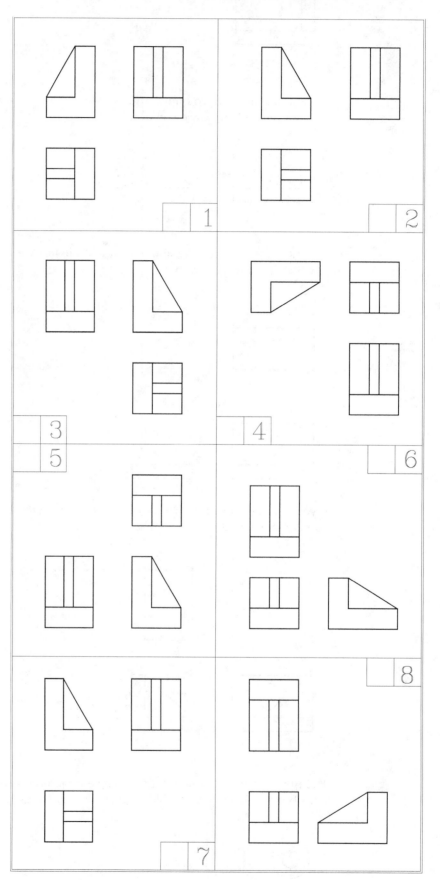

Exercise 3.3   *Insertion of missing details and hidden lines into given drawings*

Examine carefully the eight orthographic drawings of engineering components.
   Each has some lines missing. The missing lines may be hidden edges or outlines.
Add to the drawings the missing details.
   The first drawing is shown completed in the margin for your guidance.

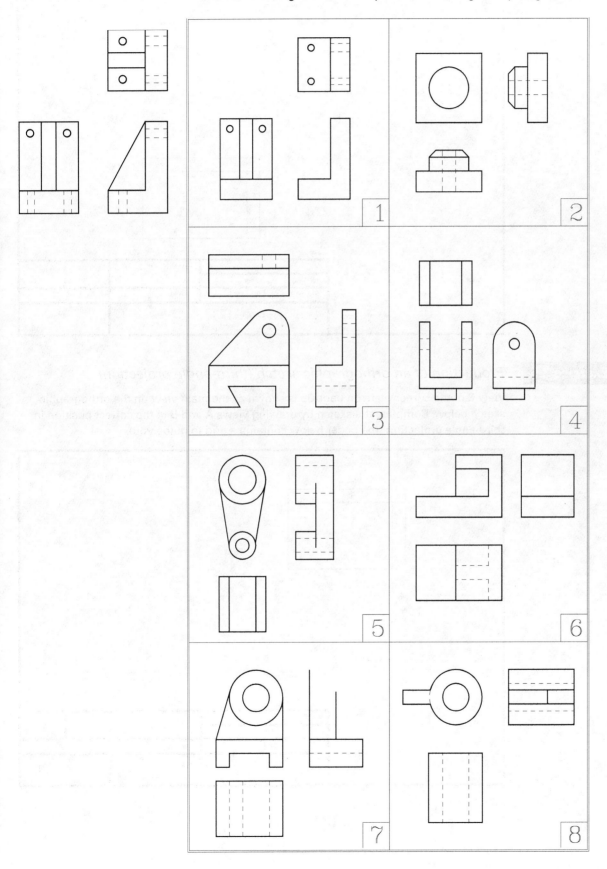

Exercise 3.4 *Production of an orthographic sketch (first-angle projection)*

View C of the corner plate on page 39 is shown as the main view on the orthographic sketch below. Complete the sketch by drawing views A and B in the correct position in **first-angle projection** (the paper below contains a grid to guide you).

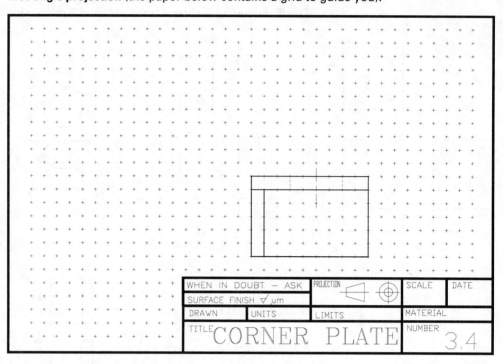

Exercise 3.5 *Production of an orthographic sketch (third-angle projection)*

View C of the corner plate on page 39 is shown as the main view on the orthographic sketch below. Complete the sketch by drawing views A and B in the correct position in **third-angle projection** (the paper below contains a grid to guide you).

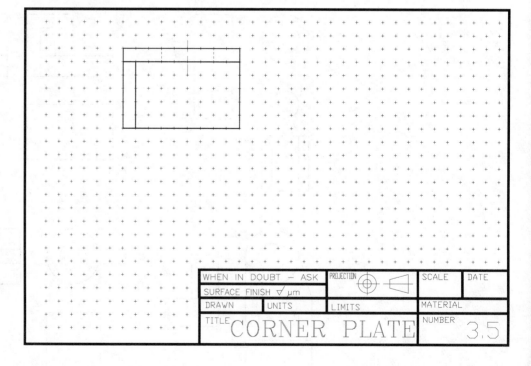

Dimensioning drawings

An engineering drawing contains information about the shape of a component. It also shows dimensions regarding the sizes and limits to which the component should be manufactured. In this book all dimensions are in millimetres (mm) unless otherwise stated. Information regarding dimensions must be clear and in accordance with BS 308, the fundamental requirements of which are described below:

- When applying dimensions to a drawing, use thin continuous dimension lines, projection lines and leaders.
- Arrowheads on dimension lines and leaders must be solid and slender.
- Dimension lines should not cross each other.
- When adding notes to a drawing, the letters, numbers and symbols should be bold and clear, not less than 3 mm in height. Capital letters are generally preferred.

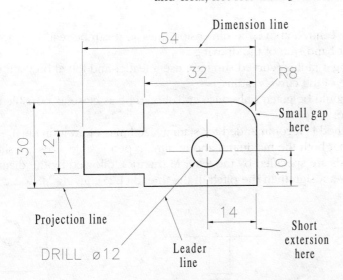

ABCDEFGHIJKLM
NOPQRSTUVWXYZ
1234567890
ø ° ±

- When applying dimensions to a drawing, all distances in each direction must be taken from the same face, line or point. This face, line or point is called a **datum**. The height, length and width measurements all have separate datums. *Note*: On these three examples only one type of datum is shown for each drawing. In practice a drawing may show more than one type of datum, e.g. a datum line and a datum face.

  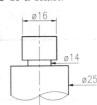

Datum faces
Also known as datum edges, they are the most common type of datum. All lengths are dimensioned from face A, all heights from face B

Datum lines
All dimensions are relative to a line. Lengths are dimensioned from Line A, heights from Line B

Datum points
Used to dimension features which all have the same reference point, P

- The symbol ∅ preceding a dimension indicates a diameter.
- There are several methods of dimensioning circles. Choose according to the size and location of the circle, and whether dimensioning a hole or a shaft.

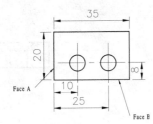 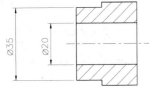 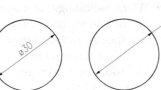

- Dimensions and text should be placed outside the drawing outline wherever possible.

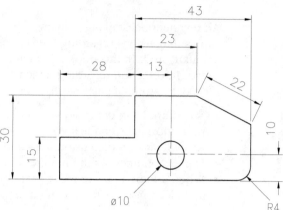

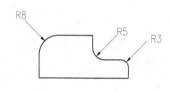

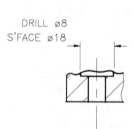

- The text should be centred above the dimension lines so it can be read from the bottom or the right-hand side of the drawing.
- When dimensioning a radius (curved surface), use a leader and the abbreviation R to precede the size of the curve's radius.
- Each dimension should be given only once and should be as close as possible to the relevant feature.
- The illustrated method is recommended for stating size limits of an individual dimension. Note that both the maximum and minimum permissible sizes are shown.
- Metric screw threads are specified by the letter M (metric) followed by the diameter of the thread (M8), a × sign then the pitch of the thread (1.25), giving M8 × 1.25.

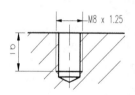

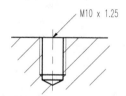

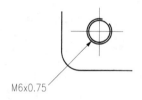

- Holes for fasteners or for locating devices should be dimensioned by one of the alternative methods shown for each type of hole.

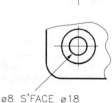

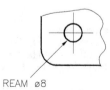

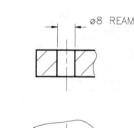

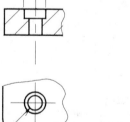

| Spot face | Ream | Counterbore | Countersink |

- When indicating that a surface is to be machined, the machining symbol is drawn on the surface or its projection line.
- If a specific surface texture is required, the roughness average (Ra) value is written on top of the machining symbol. There is more information about surface texture and roughness averages in Chapter 4. The illustrated surface is to be machined to an Ra of 3.2 μm.

Cast iron bracket

Production of a first-angle projection sketch with BS dimensions and types of line

A pictorial view of a cast iron bracket is shown in the diagram.

1. Sketch the bracket to a suitable scale so it is in good proportion in first-angle projection on the blank page provided.

2. Add dimensions to your sketch in accordance with BS 308 using the following as datums:

   (a) Height from underside
   (b) Length from front face
   (c) Widths from rear face

3. Complete the title block by adding:

   (a) Your initials
   (b) Material specification
   (c) Limits of ± 0.5 mm (plus or minus 0.5 mm)
   (d) Surface finish to be 1.6 μm

   (e) Projection symbol for first-angle projection
   (f) Scale used
   (g) Today's date

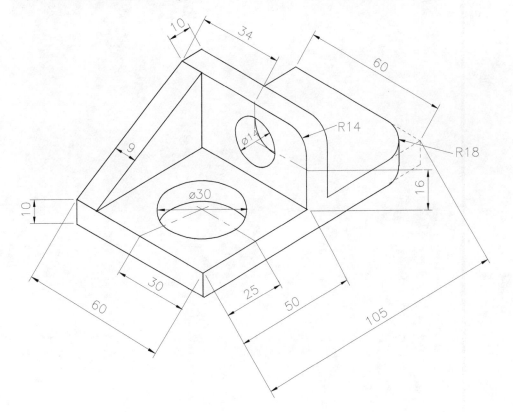

BS 308 drawing conventions

Identification of BS 308 drawing conventions

[See also Exercise 7.2 Handling engineering information]

Refer to BS 308 or other appropriate sources of information and complete the sketches in the right-hand column to show the BS convention for the illustrated features. In each case state the source of the information used and how it was verified up to date. The convention for an external screw thread has been completed for your guidance.

		DATE
	SCALE	
WHEN IN DOUBT – ASK	PROJECTION	
SURFACE FINISH ▽ μm		
	DRAWN	UNITS mm	LIMITS
		MATERIAL
TITLE CAST IRON BRACKET		NUMBER 3.6

Title	Feature	BS convention	Information source
External screw thread			
Internal screw thread			
Diamond knurling			
Ball and roller bearings			
Square on a shaft			
Flat on a shaft			
Holes on a circular pitch			

BS 308 drawing abbreviations

Exercise 3.8

Identification of BS 308 drawing abbreviations

[See also Exercise 7.2 Handling engineering information]

Refer to BS 308 : Part 1 or other appropriate source of information and complete the table below by inserting the BS symbol or abbreviation for the features shown in the drawing. In each case state the source of the information used and how it was verified up to date. The first row of the table has been completed for your guidance.

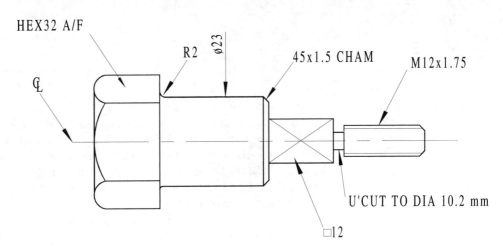

Feature shown on the drawing	BS symbol or abbreviation	Information source
Hexagon	HEX	BS 308 Part 1 Kept in college library
Across Flats (measurement of hexagon)		
Radius (Corner fillet)		
Diameter (with numbers)		
Undercut		
Diameter (with words)		
Chamfered (bevelled edge)		
Square (with numbers)		
Metric screw thread specification		
Centre line		

Sectioning

A sectional elevation may be of benefit when a drawing contains so much hidden detail that it has become unclear. A sectional elevation is a view of part of a component when viewed on a cutting plane. The cutting plane on engineering drawings is shown as a fine chain line with thick ends; the viewing direction is indicted by two arrows against these ends with identifying letters, e.g. A–A.

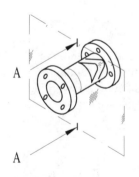

Diagramatic view of cutting plane A–A

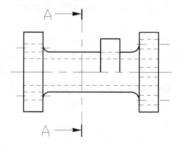

Cam flange

End view in first-angle projection

Section A–A

Consider the cam flange shown above. When the end view is drawn in first-angle projection, the resulting drawing contains much hidden detail. Compare this with the sectional view A–A, this would be seen if the cam flange were viewed on the cutting plane (all material to the left of the cutting plane is ignored). View A–A shows more clearly the wall thickness of the tube, the shape of the cam and the positions of the holes in the right-hand flange. The area through which the cutting plane passes is hatched with fine lines drawn at 45°, usually about 4 mm apart.

The layout of a sectional view is always in accordance with the rules for orthographic projection. For example, the cam flange shown above is in first-angle projection, i.e. it is viewed in the direction of the arrows A, so the sectional view is drawn opposite the side from which it is viewed.

Do not hatch these features when a cutting plane passes lengthways through them:

- Webs (supporting ribs)
- Fasteners (nuts, bolts and washers etc.)
- Shafts
- Thin sheets

When a component is sectioned through a hole or other similar feature, the hatching lines on all the areas of that component have the same pitch (spacing) and angle.

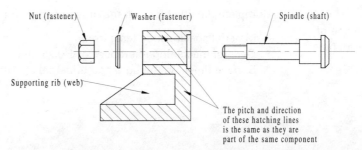

Unhatched items – the web, the shaft, and the fasteners

| Exercise 3.9 | *Recognition of sectional views in orthographic projection* |

Pick the correct sectional view from the alternatives A to Q to suit each of the eight drawings below. Sketch the correct sectional view in the appropriate space and insert its key letter in the box provided. The first drawing has been completed for your guidance.

Note: Some drawings are in first-angle projection; some in third-angle projection.

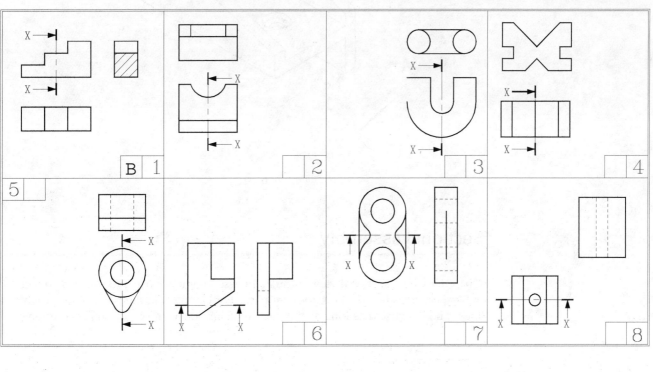

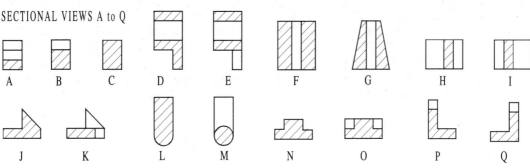

SECTIONAL VIEWS A to Q

Foot support

Production of a third-angle projection sketch with BS dimensions and a sectional view

On the blank page provided, produce a fully dimensioned third-angle projection sketch with a sectional elevation on cutting plane B–B of the foot support shown below. Refer to the previous notes about dimensioning methods, BS 308 and the sample drawing in Appendix V. Your sketch must contain fractional imperial units from the tabulated datums.

Datum	Position
Height	Underside of flat surface
Length	Centreline of Ø50 mm hole
Width	Rear face

Complete the title block on the drawing sheet for:

- Material specification (cast iron)
- General machining tolerances of ± 0.25 mm
- Surface finish on the bore and underside to have an Ra of 1.6 µm

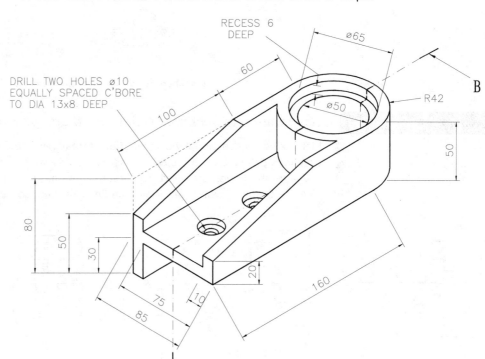

Sectional assembly

When drawing a sectional view through an assembly it is correct to draw the direction of hatching lines reversed for adjacent parts. For clarification the pitch of the hatching lines can be adjusted as long as the pitch remains constant for any single component.

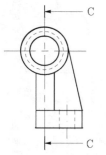

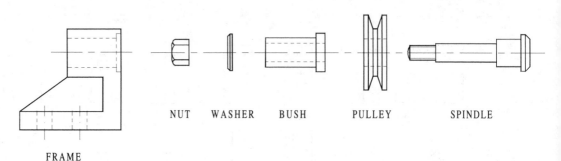

DATE

SCALE

MATERIAL

NUMBER **3.10**

PROJECTION

LIMITS

WHEN IN DOUBT — ASK

SURFACE FINISH ▽ μm

UNITS mm

DRAWN

TITLE FOOT SUPPORT

These drawings are the component parts of a pulley mounting bracket.

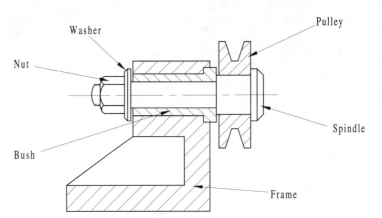

Sectioned assembly looking on cutting plane C–C of the pulley mounting bracket above. Note that the pin, nut and washer are *not* hatched.

Depth gauge

Exercise 3.11

Production of an orthographic sectional assembly sketch

Shown below are the components required to assemble a depth gauge. On the blank page provided, produce a sectional assembly sketch of the depth gauge as viewed on plane D–D. Your sketch must be clear, in good proportion and in accordance with BS 308.

The sketch can be in either first- or third-angle projection. Complete the title block with the appropriate symbol to indicate which form of orthographic projection is used.

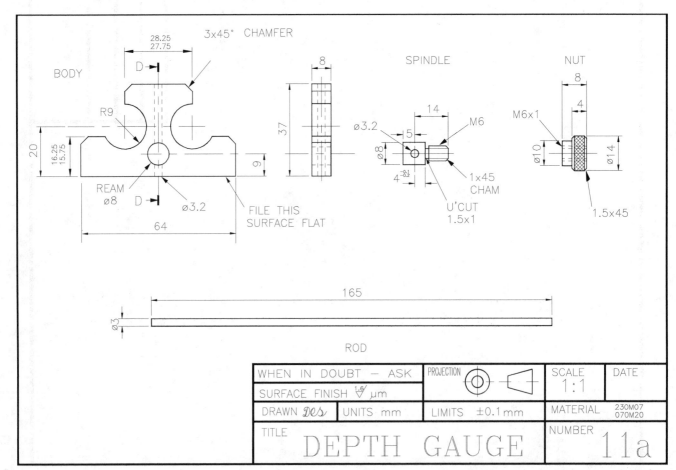

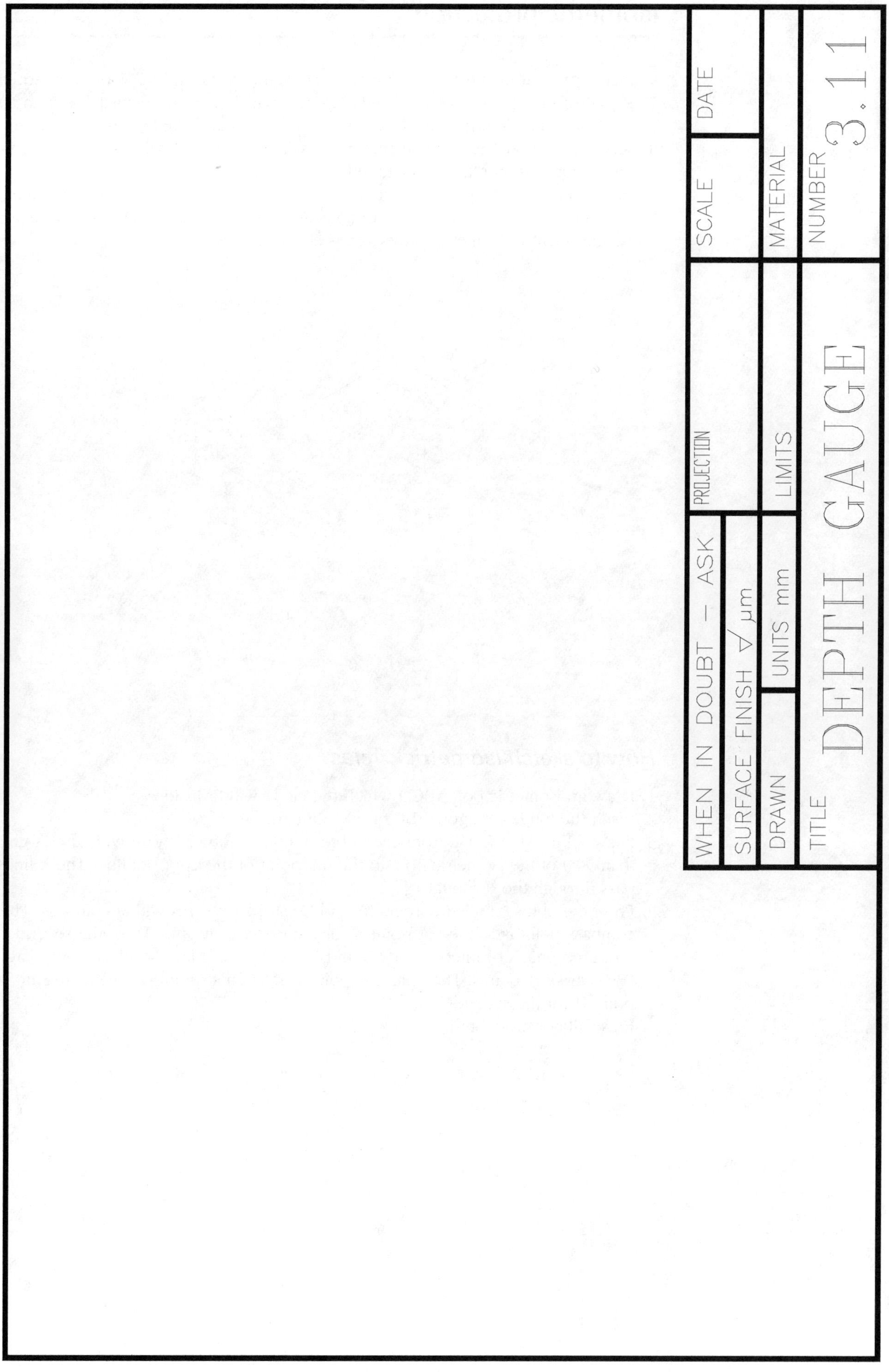

WHEN IN DOUBT — ASK

SCALE | DATE

PROJECTION

SURFACE FINISH ▽ μm

MATERIAL

LIMITS

DRAWN | UNITS mm

NUMBER 3.11

TITLE DEPTH GAUGE

Isometric projection

Isometric projection is used when a pictorial shape of the finished object is required. This type of projection shows a 3D like image, which is easier to visualise than an orthographic drawing. It is used extensively in books and catalogues as it can be understood by non-engineers. Isometric drawings are not usually used for production so dimensions are not always included.

On isometric drawings **all** horizontal lines on the X and Y planes are drawn at 30°. Vertical lines are drawn vertically. All lines are drawn to a constant scale. An example of a component in isometric projection is shown below.

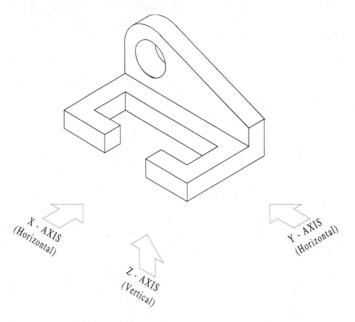

How to sketch isometric circles

1. Draw an isometric box ABCD which the circle will fit inside.
2. Insert the longest diagonal BC of the isometric box.
3. Draw a line AF and DE from each obtuse-angled corner (those with angles greater than 90°) of the isometric box, to the midpoint of the opposite line. These lines pass through the diagonal.
4. From the obtuse-angled corners (A and D) strike two arcs with a compass. The compass point is located at point A for the first arc, at point D for the second.
5. From the points of intersection (G and H) of the short lines with the long diagonal (BC), strike two arcs. The compass point is located at point G for the first arc, at point H for the second.
6. Erase all construction lines.

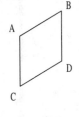

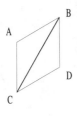

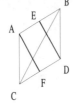

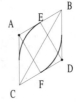

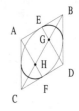

| 1 | 2 | 3 | 4 | 5 | 6 |

Angle plate

Production of an isometric sketch on isometric drawing-paper

Shown below is an angle plate drawn in first-angle projection. Sketch below an isometric view of the angle plate. The page has an isometric grid for your guidance. Use a scale of one space on the grid to represent 0.25 in of the angle plate (4:1). Take care to start in a suitable place on the page so as not to run out of paper.

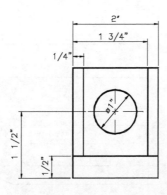

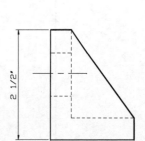

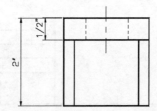

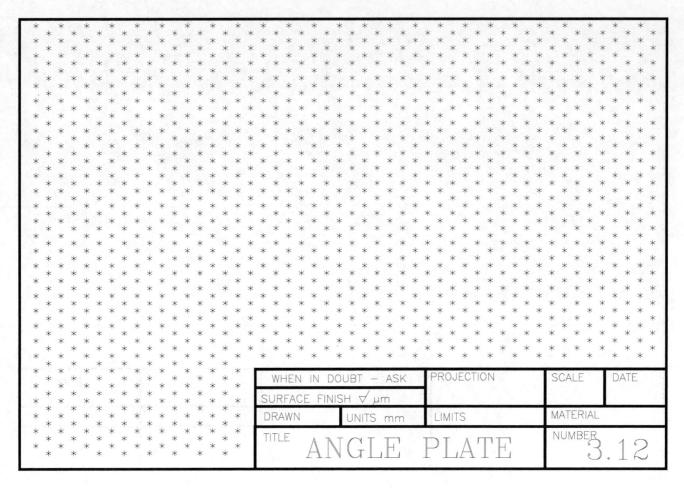

WHEN IN DOUBT — ASK		PROJECTION		SCALE	DATE
SURFACE FINISH ∇ μm					
DRAWN	UNITS mm	LIMITS		MATERIAL	
TITLE	ANGLE PLATE			NUMBER	3.12

Milling clamp

Production of an isometric sketch of a component

On the blank page provided, sketch the milling clamp shown below. Your sketch must be in isometric projection, in good proportion and in accordance with BS 308. Dimension your sketch in millimetres so it can be clearly understood.

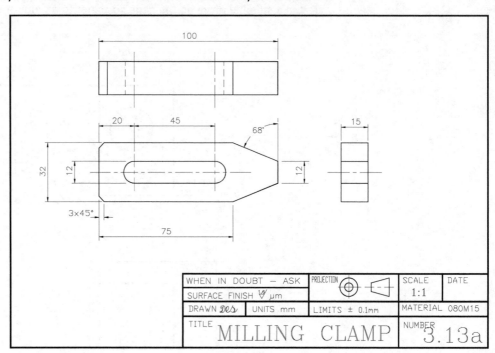

WHEN IN DOUBT — ASK	PROJECTION	SCALE	DATE
SURFACE FINISH ᵛ μm	⊕ ◁	1:1	
DRAWN *Des*	UNITS mm	LIMITS ± 0.1mm	MATERIAL 080M15
TITLE MILLING CLAMP			NUMBER 3.13a

WHEN IN DOUBT — ASK	PROJECTION	SCALE	DATE
SURFACE FINISH ∇ μm	ISOMETRIC		
DRAWN	UNITS mm	LIMITS	MATERIAL
TITLE MILLING CLAMP			NUMBER 3.13

Milling clamp set

Exercise 3.14

Production of an isometric sketch of an assembly

Study the component parts of the milling clamp set shown below. On the blank page provided, sketch the milling clamp set as it would be used on a milling machine table when clamping a workpiece. Your sketch should be in isometric projection and in good proportion.

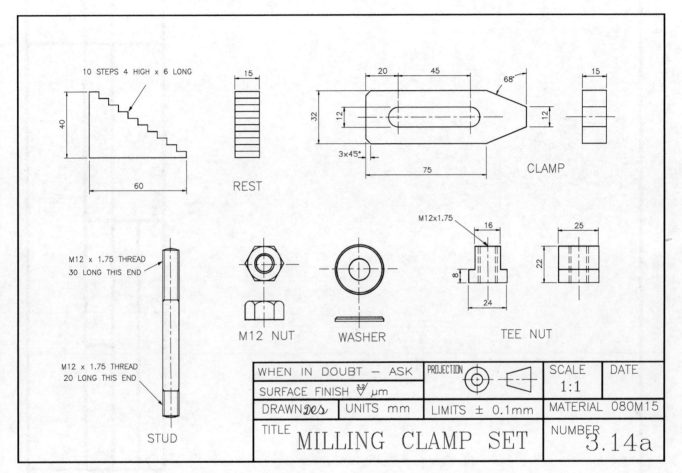

WHEN IN DOUBT — ASK

PROJECTION

SURFACE FINISH ∇ μm

UNITS mm

LIMITS

DRAWN

SCALE

DATE

MATERIAL

TITLE
MILLING CLAMP SET

NUMBER
3.14

Exercise 3.15   *Engineering drawing test*

The multiple choice question paper will only be issued to candidates by their supervisor on satisfactory completion of the appropriate exercises. The answer sheet below must be completed by the candidate when the questions are issued.

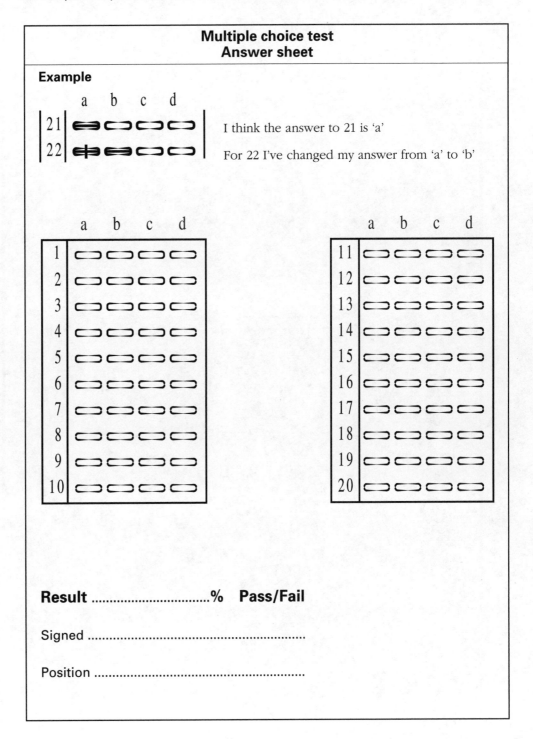

Chapter 4

Basic engineering measurement

Exercise		Page	Date	Signed by Trainer
4.1	Interpretation of limits of size	65		
4.2	Knowledge of defective tool reporting procedure	66		
4.3	Measurement of length using an engineer's rule	66		
4.4	Measurement of length using a steel tape rule	67		
4.5	Measurement of features using calipers and a rule	68		
4.6	Measurement of angles using a workshop protractor	71		
4.7	Profile measurement using radius and screw pitch gauges	72		
4.8	Reading micrometers in metric and imperial units	74		
4.9	Use of micrometers to measure components	76		
4.10	Readings of vernier scales in metric and imperial units	79		
4.11	Measurement of features using vernier instruments	80		
4.12	Measurement using feeler gauges	82		
4.13	Assessment of surface texture using comparison plates	83		
4.14	Selection and use of a range of measuring tools	83		
4.15	Measurement test	85		
All information presented in this section is complete, accurate and legible				
All information presented in this section is in the format required				

The importance of measuring is widespread; different quantities are measured according to the task in hand, e.g. cooks measure weight, athletes measure time and electronics engineers measure amps, volts and resistance. For the mechanical engineer, length is the most important measurement. The standard unit of length in Great Britain, Europe and most of the world is the ISO (International Standards Organisation) metric metre (m). This unit is generally too large for engineering purposes, so it is divided into 1000 equal parts called **millimetres** (**mm**).

1 m = 1000 mm

This workbook deals mainly with the metric system of measurement. The most common imperial units of length used in engineering are the inch (in or ") and the foot (ft or '). These are extensively used in the United States and Great Britain, and for American contracts and maintenance work of old equipment. Imperial units are often stated as fractions of an inch (3/4 in) or in decimals (0.75 in). As many British companies have American connections, British engineers must know both the metric and the imperial systems of measurement.

To convert millimetres to inches, multiply by 0.039
To convert inches to millimetres, multiply by 25.4

Appendices I and II of this workbook are conversion tables for converting millimetres to inches and inches to millimetres.

Engineering measurements need to be accurate. Inaccuracies can be caused by expansion of materials due to temperature change. To avoid these errors, all precision measurements should be taken at a standard temperature of 20 °C (68 °F).

Size limits on components

It is physically impossible to make any part *exactly* to any size. There must always be some allowance for errors, however slight. The correct term for this allowance is the **limits of size**, often called the limits. There are always two limits to represent the maximum and the minimum permissible size to which any component feature can be made.

General limits of size are shown on engineering drawings in the title block. They refer to all dimensions. Any feature that has other limits than those indicated in the title block is indicated by one of the methods in the diagram below.

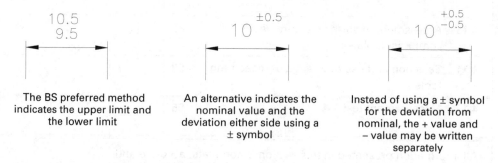

The BS preferred method indicates the upper limit and the lower limit

An alternative indicates the nominal value and the deviation either side using a ± symbol

Instead of using a ± symbol for the deviation from nominal, the + value and – value may be written separately

All these examples show a feature of diameter 10 mm. The finished component must have a diameter of between 9.5 mm and 10.5 mm for it to be acceptable.

The names of the component parts that make up the dimension are:

1. The **nominal** size; the nearest whole millimetre (or fractional inch) size of the feature – 10 mm in the examples above.
2. The maximum permissible size; called the **high limit** (or top limit) – 10.5 mm in the examples above.
3. The minimum permissible size; called the **low limit** (or bottom limit) – 9.5 mm in the examples above.
4. The **tolerance**; the difference between the limits of size – in the above examples, it is the difference between 9.5 mm and 10.5 mm (1 mm).

| **Exercise 4.1** | *Interpretation of limits of size* |

From the drawing of the three dimensioned features on a pulley assembly, examine the dimensions carefully and complete the table below. For items with small tolerances there is a higher production cost, so designers only put small tolerances on components when it is absolutely necessary.

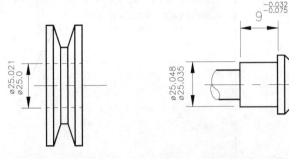

	Pulley hole	**Shaft length**	**Shaft diameter**
Nominal size			
High limit			
Low limit			
Tolerance			

Engineering measuring tools

A wide range of length measuring tools is available to engineers. After looking at the component's features to be measured and considering the accuracy required, a decision on which tool is best suited to measuring is made. This decision is made with reference to:

- Required accuracy
- Linear or angular dimension
- Access to the feature
- Shape of feature
- Size of feature

To make accurate measurements and to ensure appropriate readings are being given, it is always necessary to use high quality measuring tools, which must be stored and maintained correctly. Store measuring tools safely in their original case and in a clean dry place when not in use. Before using measuring tools, it is good practice to check the accuracy of the instrument against a gauge of known size. If any error is suspected, it should be reported to the supervisor at the earliest opportunity to reduce any wastage which would otherwise be caused. Remember that the inaccuracy could be your fault, so a back-footed approach may be appropriate.

When reporting defective tools to the supervisor, the best approach is to say that you need advice because you think something could be causing a measurement error. This type of approach will usually be better received than just saying the tool is wrong or inaccurate. If there is such a company procedure to follow, it must be adhered to at all times.

Exercise 4.2

Knowledge of defective tool reporting procedure

Find out the procedure for reporting suspect and defective measuring tools. If there is a printed form for completing your report, make a sketch of it or attach it to the page.

Procedure for reporting a possibly defective measuring tool	Defective tool report

When in use, tools should always be kept away from oil and dirt, and the possibility of being damaged. Some of the most common measuring tools are described on the following pages, together with typical applications and uses. Remember, tools borrowed from the company store or from workmates should be treated with the greatest care and respect. Always return borrowed tools in good order, in a clean condition and within a reasonable timescale.

The engineer's rule

Engineer's rules are widely available in 150 mm (6 in) and 300 mm (12 in) lengths, although other lengths are available. Better quality rules are made from tempered stainless steel and have a non-glare satin chrome finish. Rules usually have both metric and imperial graduations engraved on alternate sides. The edges of rules are ground flat to allow straightness to be assessed. Rules are the quickest way to measure components to within about ±0.5 mm (0.02 in) and are used extensively for making rough measurements. The finest millimetre division marked on metric scales is normally 0.5 mm, imperial scales are normally calibrated to 1/64 in (0.0156 in). In practice these graduations are very difficult to see.

A typical 150 mm (6 in) engineer's rule

Exercise 4.3

Measurement of length using an engineer's rule

Measure the length and width of this page as accurately as possible with a steel engineer's rule.

- Metric.

The page height is...............mm   The width is...............mm

The finest metric reading possible on the rule is...............mm

- Imperial.
The page height is...............inches   The width is...............inches

The finest inch reading possible on the rule is...............inches (fractional)

Tape rules

Roll-up tapes are used for measuring long lengths up to a maximum of 30 m (100 ft). Measuring tapes are supplied with imperial and metric scales painted onto a steel blade. Shorter tapes of about 3 m (10 ft) may be graduated in 0.5 mm (1/32 in) intervals whereas longer tapes may be calibrated in 1 mm (1/16 in) intervals only. It is difficult to read a tape over a long distance accurately as the tape may sag, expand or not be held straight. A tape rule would be suited to checking the length of steel barstock on delivery or for measuring the length of pipework systems.

Exercise 4.4

Measurement of length using a steel tape rule

Measure a door with a steel tape rule.

The workshop door is...............mm high   The workshop door is...............mm long

The steel tape rule's finest metric calibrations are...............mm

The workshop door is...............inches high   The workshop door is...............inches long

The steel tape rule's finest imperial calibrations are...............inch

Calipers

Calipers are tools which have two high quality steel arms with rounded ends. They are used to measure features which are inaccessible with other tools. The distance between the ends of the arms can be adjusted to fit a component's size (either externally or internally). The size is then *transferred* to a suitable measuring tool (e.g. an engineer's rule or a micrometer) and a reading taken. Calipers are non-indicating tools because they have no graduations to indicate size. Due to the transfer of size, calipers cannot be as accurate as direct measuring tools, but accuracies of about ±0.5 mm (1/64 in) are readily achieved. With care and practice more accurate readings can be attained. Both internal and external calipers are made as either spring or firm-joint type, they are set and used as shown below:

Spring-type calipers

The legs of this type of caliper are opened or closed by means of the adjusting nut. They pivot on a roller and are tensioned by a bow spring. The external type shown is available in sizes from 75 mm (3 in) to 300 mm (12 in). Common uses for external calipers are measuring diameters of pipes, recessed bores and undercuts which would otherwise be inaccessible.

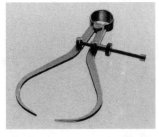

Spring type external calipers

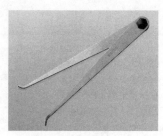

Firm joint type internal calipers

Firm-joint calipers

The caliper legs on the firm-joint type pivot on a large screw which incorporates fibre washers. These washers enable the settings to be retained. Adjustment for the size to be measured is made by opening or closing the legs by hand to the approximate size, then tapping one leg on a solid surface to make the final adjustment. The size of this type of caliper ranges from 150 mm (6 in) to 600 mm (24 in).

Transferring measurements with calipers

When transferring a measurement, the caliper legs are set to touch the work's maximum dimension. The size is then transferred to a rule or micrometer and checked as shown:

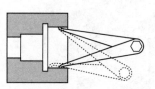

Set the caliper in the bore

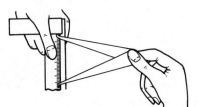

Read off the bore size

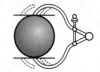

Set the caliper on a diameter

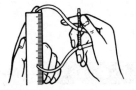

Read off the diameters size

Exercise 4.5 Measurement of features using calipers and a rule

Obtain the **jig buttons** and the **knurled locking screws** from the tool store and use calipers and a good quality steel rule to measure all the required dimensions as accurately as possible in metric and imperial units. Fill in the tables with your readings.

Eccentric jig button

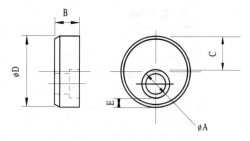

Jig button

	ØA	B	C	ØD	E
mm					
inch					

Knurled locking screw

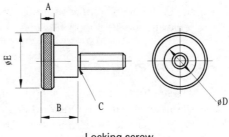

Locking screw

	A	B	C	ØD	ØE
mm					
inch					

The engineer's square

There are three types of square in common use; try squares, cylinder squares and box squares. Try squares and cylinder squares are described here, the box square is described in Chapter 5.

Try square

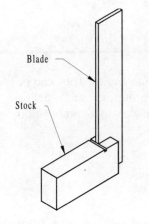

Blade

Stock

A typical engineers try square

A valuable tool, the try square is used on nearly all jobs for assessing squareness. Try squares consist of two parts; a thin parallel blade and a short, thick base called the **stock**. The two pieces are assembled so that both edges of the blade are square to both edges of the stock.

Try squares are available in a range of blade lengths (from 75 mm to 600 mm), and grades to BS 939 (AA reference, A inspection and B workshop grades). All try squares must be handled and stored carefully to retain their accuracy. Try squares can be used for checking the squareness of workpiece corners and also for marking out (Chapter 5). The workshop grade (B) is the most popular type and is made to an accuracy of 0.0083 mm per 1000 mm length of blade. The blade on this type is hardened and tempered but the stock is left soft.

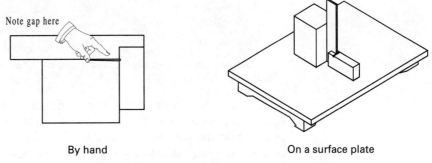

Note gap here

By hand

On a surface plate

Testing a workpiece for squareness with a try square

To check the squareness of a workpiece using a try square, hold the work against the stock of the square and slide it towards the blade until contact is made. The assembly can then be held up and viewed towards light to visually assess the size of any gap or error. This procedure can be undertaken by hand (above left) or on a surface plate (above right).

As engineer's try squares are non-indicating tools, a measuring device must be used in order to find the actual deviation from square (90°). A suitable measuring tool is a feeler gauge. The procedure for measuring errors of squareness is described in the feeler gauge section of this chapter.

Cylinder square

These tools are case-hardened cylinders which have been ground so the outside diameter is parallel. One end is ground so it is square to the outside diameter. A typical cylinder square is about 300 mm high and Ø75 mm. This type of square can be used on a surface plate for setting workpieces upright. Cylinder squares are sometimes preferred to try squares because they are more stable than try squares, and they are easier to make and restore.

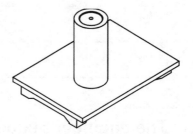

A cylinder square on a surface plate

Workshop protractors

Workshop protractors are instruments for setting and measuring angles. They can be read to an accuracy of about ±1/2° (±30′ of arc). Workshop protractors are usually supplied as part of a combination set. The components that make up a combination set are:

- Hardened steel rule (usually 300 mm)
- Moving protractor head which incorporates a spirit level
- Square head with 45° edge and a spirit level
- Centre head

A combination set is shown below in some typical measuring situations.

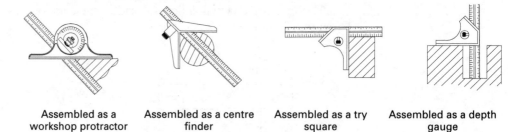

| Assembled as a workshop protractor | Assembled as a centre finder | Assembled as a try square | Assembled as a depth gauge |

To read a workshop protractor, first set the instrument so the edge of the rule is in contact with one side of the work and the protractor head's measuring surface is in contact with the other surface of the work. The protractor scale is then locked in position and examined to see which angular division lines up with the zero line on the protractor head.

Although there is only one row of 180 calibrations (lines) on the moving protractor head, it is labelled in two directions:

0° to 180° and 180° to 0°

By reading the most appropriate scale, the angle can be read as shown in the examples below.

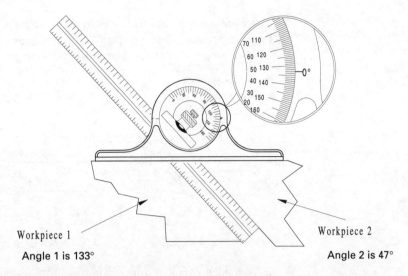

Workpiece 1

Angle 1 is 133°

Workpiece 2

Angle 2 is 47°

Exercise 4.6   *Measurement of angles using a workshop protractor*

Examine the (magnified) workshop protractor readings for workpieces 3 and 4 below and write their angle in the space provided.

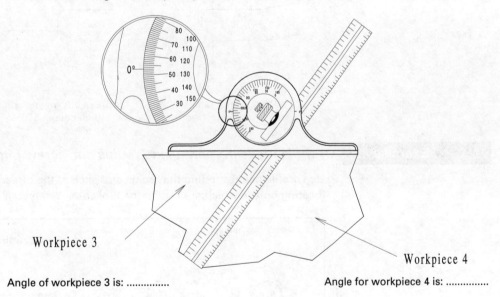

Workpiece 3

Workpiece 4

Angle of workpiece 3 is: ....

Angle for workpiece 4 is: ....

Use a workshop protractor to measure the angle on the items below.

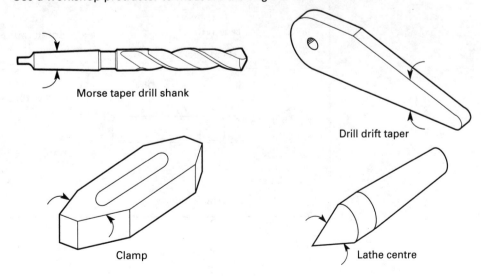

Morse taper drill shank

Drill drift taper

Clamp

Lathe centre

Profile gauges

These instruments are for assessing the accuracy of shapes. Profile gauges are made to have an accurate shape or profile. Profile gauges are usually supplied in sets that cover a range of profiles. The most common profile gauges are:

- radius gauges
- screw pitch gauges
- point angle gauges

| Radius gauges | Screw pitch gauges | Point angle gauges |

In use, each gauge is selected in turn from the appropriate set and compared with the work. The gauge is then held against the job and viewed with daylight in the background. The differences in profile can easily be seen and assessment made as to the quality of the work surface.

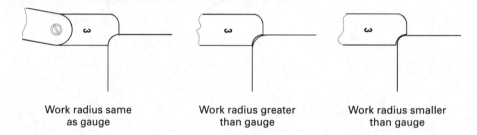

| Work radius same as gauge | Work radius greater than gauge | Work radius smaller than gauge |

Exercise 4.7

Profile measurement using radius and screw pitch gauges

Use profile gauges to find the radius and pitch of the threads on the **hand screw** and the **locating button** which are kept in the tool store. Write your answers in the table below.

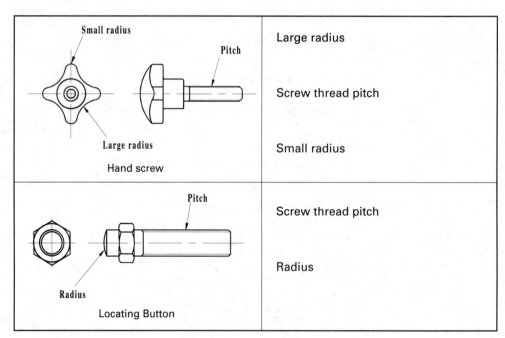

Small radius	Large radius
Pitch	
Hand screw	Screw thread pitch
	Small radius
Locating Button	Screw thread pitch
Pitch	
Radius	Radius

Micrometer instruments

All micrometer instruments can measure features to within 0.01 mm (0.001 in), although some are more accurate. There are several different types of micrometer (see page 75), but the most common type is the external fixed-anvil type, used for measuring outside (external) dimensions. This type of micrometer has a rigid bow-shaped frame, a micrometer head and a fixed anvil (measuring face). External micrometers are available in a range of sizes. They are also available in either metric (mm) or imperial (inch) units. External micrometers are made in the following size ranges:

0–25 mm (0–1 in)
25–50 mm (1–2 in)
50–75 mm (2–3 in)
75–100 mm (3–4 in)

and so on in 25 mm intervals to a maximum of 450 mm (18 in).
The drawing below shows the names of the parts of a micrometer.

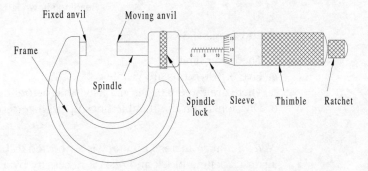

A standard 0–25 mm metric micrometer

Micrometers are manufactured to small tolerances and they should always be carefully handled. Always ensure the anvils are clean because appreciable errors can be caused by dirt and oil on the anvils. Clean by lightly squeezing a piece of paper between the anvils and sliding it out, the dirt or grease is then removed.

Setting and reading an external metric micrometer

1. Identify the size of the micrometer required, noting the lower limit.
2. Using the ratchet, adjust the micrometer so its anvils are both in contact with the component being measured.
3. Set the 'measuring pressure' with the ratchet.
   Count the number of whole millimetre divisions visible on the sleeve.
4. Add on 0.5 mm if a 1/2 mm division is visible on the sleeve.
5. Add on 0.01 mm for each thimble division.

Total the values recorded above to get the reading. See the example below.

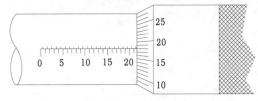

Reading is 21.68 mm

1. The lower limit is	0
3. The number of visible whole divisions is	21
4. A 0.5 mm is visible	0.5
5. Division 18 on the thimble lines up with zero on the sleeve	0.18
Total	**21.68 mm**

Setting and reading an external imperial micrometer

1. Identify the size range of micrometer required, noting the lower limit.
2. Adjust the micrometer so that its anvils are both in contact with the component being measured.
3. Set the 'measuring pressure' with the ratchet.
4. Count how many 0.1 in divisions are visible on the sleeve.
5. Count how many 0.025 in divisions are visible between the edge of the thimble and the last recorded 0.1 in mark.
6. Record 0.001 in for each thimble division.
7. Total the values recorded above to get the reading.

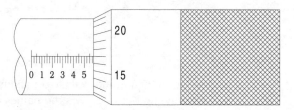

Reading shown is 1.592 in

The example shows:

1. The lower limit is		1.00
4. Five 0.1 divisions are visible		0.5
5. There are three 0.025 in marks visible before the thimble edge		0.075
6. Division 17 on the thimble lines up with zero on the sleeve		0.017
	Total	**1.592 in**

Note: If a micrometer's accuracy is suspected to be incorrect, it should be checked against a setting block and reset if necessary by a suitably qualified person.

Exercise 4.8

Reading micrometers in metric and imperial units

Look at the three metric and three imperial micrometer settings below and write the indicated measurement in the space underneath each diagram.

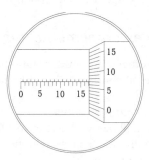

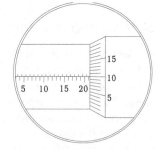

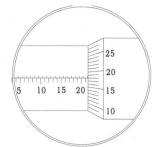

1. 0–25 mm micrometer

Reading ....

2. 25–50 mm micrometer

Reading ....

3. 75–100 mm micrometer

Reading ....

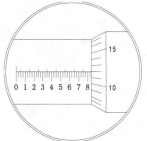

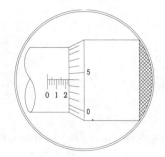

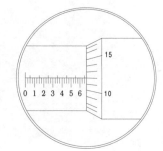

4. 0–1 in micrometer

Reading ....

5. 2–3 in micrometer

Reading ....

6. 1–2 in micrometer

Reading ....

Other types of micrometer

As well as the usual external micrometer, other types are also available. Although less common, these instruments are valuable and accurate measuring tools. Three types are described below.

External adjustable micrometer

External adjustable micrometers have an interchangeable fixed anvil which can be replaced with other precision anvils of varying length. This extends their measuring range with minimal loss of accuracy. Reading to 0.01 mm (0.001 in) is still possible. Adjustable micrometers are usually supplied with a set of precision checking gauges.

An External adjustable micrometer with four anvils can measure from 0 to 100 mm

Depth micrometers

Depth Micrometers are used for measuring the depth of holes, slots, etc. They consist of a hardened and ground base, a micrometer head and a set of interchangeable precision rods which can be used to give a wide measuring range, typically from 0 to 300 mm (0 to 12 in).

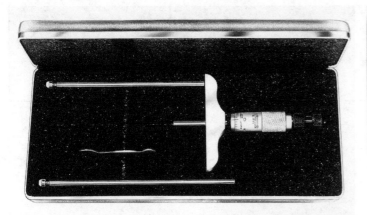

Depth micrometer set containing hardened base,
micrometer head and a range of interchangeable rods

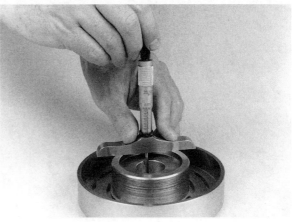

Depth micrometer in use measuring a tee slot depth

Internal micrometers

Designed to measure the internal dimensions of components, internal micrometers are also adjustable by means of a set of precision rods, giving a typical overall range of 50 to 200 mm (2 to 8 in). The head on internal micrometers usually has a shorter measuring range than the other types of micrometer (13 mm or 1/2 in). However, they still can measure to within 0.01 mm (0.001 in) over their entire range.

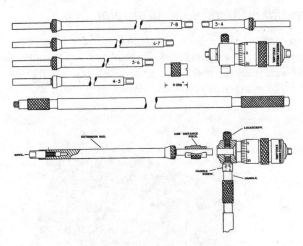

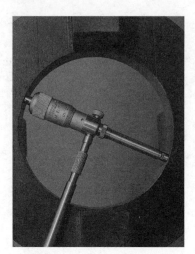

Internal micrometer set showing the measuring head, 5 precision rods, spacer and the handle

Measuring a bore with an internal micrometer

Note: Micrometer heads can be fitted into special tools and instruments for inspection and measurement.

Exercise 4.9

Use of micrometers to measure components

Use metric and imperial micrometers to assess the sizes of the **electrical cable**, a **one pence coin** and a **two pence coin**, and the **tee nut blank** which is kept in the tool store. Return tools after use promptly and in a suitable condition.

Cable size (cross-sectional area)	1 mm²	2.5 mm²
Cable diameter (mm)		
Cable diameter (inch)		

	A	B	C	D	E
mm					
inch					

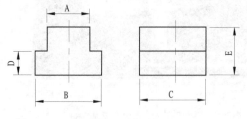

Tee nut blank

	One Pence coin		Two Pence coin	
	Diameter	**Thickness**	**Diameter**	**Thickness**
mm				
inch				

Vernier calipers

For slightly less precise measurement than the micrometer, a vernier instrument can be used. Vernier instruments have two engraved scales, a main scale and a vernier (sliding) scale. The vernier system allows fine measurements to be taken in either millimetre or inches by observing and reading the lines that coincide (line up) on the two scales. The main scale is calibrated in full-size divisions, whereas the vernier scale is calibrated in slightly smaller divisions.

Metric readings of 0.02 mm or 0.05 mm (depending on the scale) and imperial readings of 0.001 in can be reliably achieved by experienced engineers.

The most common vernier instrument is the vernier caliper. A vernier caliper is a useful tool as it has a long measuring range (150 mm, or 6 in is common) and a wide variety of applications. It can be used for the following measurements:

- External
- Internal
- Depth
- Step

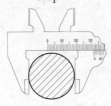 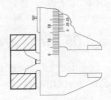 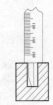 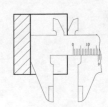

Vernier caliper used for external shaft measurement

Vernier caliper used for internal bore measurement

Vernier caliper used for depth measurement

Vernier caliper used for step measurement

The vernier caliper shown below is of a typical design. The scales have fine black lines on a satin chrome background to enable easy and accurate reading. Scales are flush fitting which reduces the chances of parallax (sighting) errors while reading. The jaws are fully hardened and their measuring surfaces accurately finished so that all measuring surfaces are parallel. The internal jaws are bevelled to reduce their contact area and to enable measurement of fine undercuts and similar features. The end of the instrument is square to the depth rod, which is thin and tapered at its end. Vernier instruments should always be carefully handled, kept clean and stored in their original cases.

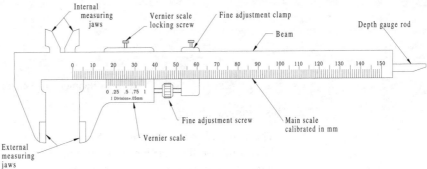

The parts on a vernier caliper

Precision vernier calipers are usually calibrated with a metric and an imperial scale, but for clarity, the calipers illustrated in this chapter are shown only with millimetres or inches.

Setting and reading vernier calipers

1. The caliper is roughly adjusted to fit the component.
2. Lock the caliper in position with the small screw on the fine adjustment clamp.
3. Turn the fine adjustment screw so the anvils are a good fit on the workpiece.
4. Lock the vernier scale into position with its locking screw.
5. Read off the measurement (see below for methods).

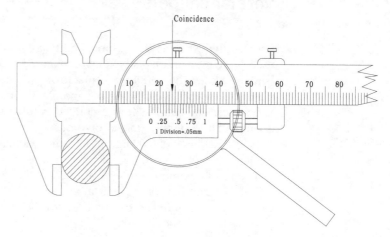

A vernier caliper set to read a metric scale (see detail below)

The method of reading each of the various vernier scales is slightly different. The procedure for reading each is described in the following three sections.

Reading a 0.05 mm vernier scale

1. Count the number of main scale divisions (usually whole millimetres) before the vernier scale zero line.
2. Look on the vernier scale and observe which 0.05 mm division coincides with (lines up with) any main scale division; it is marked with an asterisk* here.
3. Add up the above values.

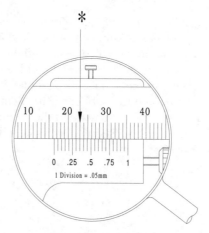

Reading is 16.40 mm

This example shows:

1. There are 16 main divisions before the zero line on the vernier scale   16
2. Division 7 on the vernier lines up with a main scale division
   Each division represents 0.05 mm, so 7 × 0.05 = 0.35   0.35

Total   **16.35 mm**

Reading a 0.02 mm vernier scale

1. Count the number of main scale divisions (usually whole millimetres) before the vernier scale zero line.
2. Look on the vernier scale and observe which 0.02 mm division coincides with (lines up with) any main scale division; it is marked with an asterisk here.
3. Add up the above values.

This example shows:

1. There are 16 main divisions before the zero line on the vernier scale   16
2. Division 9 on the vernier lines up with a main scale division
   Each division represents 0.02 mm; so 9 × 0.02 = 0.18   0.18
   Total   16.18 mm

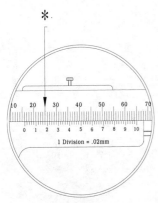

Reading is 16.18 mm

Reading an imperial vernier scale

1. Count the number of inches before the zero line on the sliding (vernier) scale.
2. Note how many 0.1 in are included between the vernier zero and the first whole inch mark on the main scale.
3. Note how many 0.025 in marks are included between the vernier zero and the last 0.1 in mark on the main scale.
4. Look on the vernier scale and note which 0.001 in division coincides with (lines up with) any main scale division; it is marked with an asterisk here.
5. Add up the above values to get the reading.

This example shows:

1. One whole inch before the zero line on the vernier scale   1
2. Two 0.1 in marks between the vernier zero and the 1 in mark   0.2
3. Three 0.025 in lines between the vernier zero and the 0.2 in mark   0.075
4. Division 18 of the vernier lines up with a main scale division
   Each vernier division represents 0.001 in, so 18 × 0.001 = 0.018   0.018
   Total   1.293 in

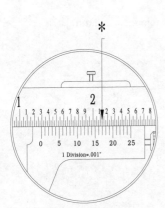

Reading is 1.293 in

Exercise 4.10

Readings of vernier scales in metric and imperial units

For each of the six vernier readings below, insert the indicated measurement in the space provided.

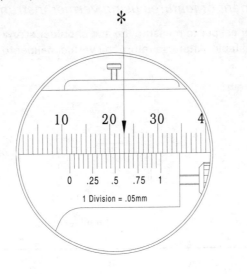

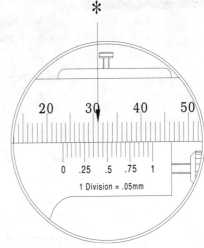

Reading...............mm   Reading...............mm

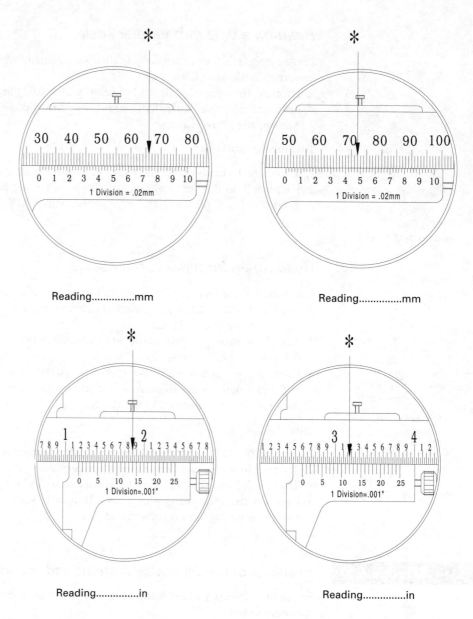

Reading...............mm

Reading...............mm

Reading...............in

Reading...............in

Measurement of features using vernier instruments

Use a vernier caliper to measure the and **shoulder screw** the **fork end** and enter your results in the table. After use return the vernier caliper to the store in its case.

Shoulder screw

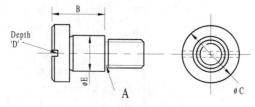

Shoulder screw

	A	B	⌀C	D	⌀E
mm					
inch					

Fork end

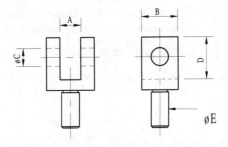

Fork end

	A	B	∅C	D	∅E
mm					
inch					

Feeler gauges

Feeler gauges are generally supplied as sets of shims (very thin pieces of high quality steel). Each shim has a different thickness and can be inserted into a small gap to assess its width.

Feeler gauges can be used to assess the amount of distortion in a steel bar after heat treatment. Put the work onto a flat surface then insert a thin feeler gauge into a gap between the work and the flat surface. If the thin gauge goes in easily, a thicker gauge is tried. The process is repeated until the thickest possible gauge is found which can be inserted; this indicates the size of the gap.

To check the accuracy of a try square, mount the cylinder square on a surface plate and hold the try square against the cylinder square. Feeler gauges can then be inserted into any gap to assess the try square's inaccuracy.

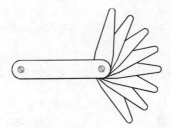

A typical set of metric feeler gauges
(0.03–1 mm)

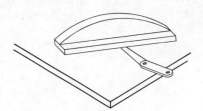

Using feeler gauges to measure
distortion

Using feeler gauges to measure clearance

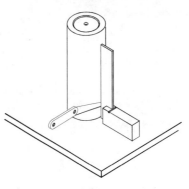

Using feeler gauges to test a try square

Exercise 4.12

Measurement using feeler gauges

Take a try square and an angle plate from the tool store and test the try square for squareness on a surface plate by using slip gauges as shown above.

Is the try square within its accepted limits? ....

Use feeler gauges to assess the gap between the sides of a standard tee nut and the machine tee slot into which it fits.

The gap is..............mm   The gap is...............inch

Surface texture comparison plates

Surface texture comparison plates are sometimes called **scratch blocks**. They are generally supplied in sets, and each plate contains several samples of surface finishes produced by various machining methods to varying degrees of surface roughness. One plate may be samples of turned diameters. Each surface will represent a specified roughness average (Ra) value. An appropriate plate is selected and compared with the roughness of the work. This is done by visual examination and by comparative scratching using a fingernail. When the surface on the plate most similar to the work is found, its quality of surface finish can be read off as a number. The number is the Ra value, given in micrometres (μm).

Good quality operations should produce the tabulated roughness averages.

Process	Ra value of finish (μm)
Grinding	0.05 – 0.8
Finish machining	0.4 – 1.6
Rough machining	3.2 – 12.5
Forging/casting	1.6 – 50

Surface texture comparison plates may be used for assessing the surface texture for most machining processes. A popular set of surface texture plates is illustrated below, it is supplied in an attractive wallet and is for the use of inspectors and draughtspersons etc.

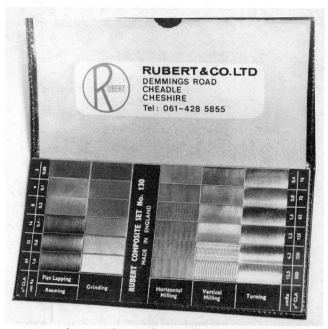

A composite set of surface texture plates

| Exercise 4.13 | *Assessment of surface texture using comparison plates* |

Use surface texture plates to assess the surface texture of the parts listed below.

Turned and faced diameters on the knurled locking screw	Turned and milled surfaces on the fork end	Cylindrically ground surfaces on the shoulder screw
Surface texture .... μm	Surface texture .... μm	Surface texture .... μm

| Exercise 4.14 | *Selection and use of a range of measuring tools* |

The **clamp** workpiece on the drawing below is kept in the stores. Examine the drawing to find the maximum and minimum permissible sizes for the various dimensions of the clamp, then insert each tolerance (most can be expressed as a ± deviation from the nominal value) into the appropriate cell of the table (overleaf).

Take the **clamp** from the store and measure all dimensions with suitable measuring instruments. Insert your choice of measuring tool and your reason for selecting that tool in the table. After measuring the clamp, you should know whether each feature is good, whether it is too big and needs reworking, or whether it is scrap.

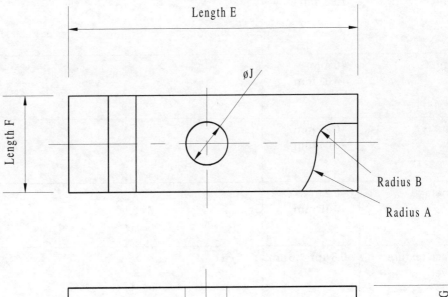

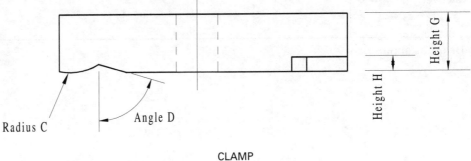

CLAMP

Dimension	Tolerance	Instrument selected	Reason	Verdict*
Radius A	±0.5 mm			good/scrap/rework
Radius B	±0.5 mm			good/scrap/rework
Radius C	±0.5 mm			good/scrap/rework
Angle D	±0.5°			good/scrap/rework
Length E	±0.4 mm			good/scrap/rework
Length F	±0.3 mm			good/scrap/rework
Length G	+0 mm −0.02 mm			good/scrap/rework
Height H	+0.25 mm −0.01 mm			good/scrap/rework
Diameter J	+0.2 mm +0.15 mm			good/scrap/rework
Surface texture all over.	0.8 µm–1.6 µm			good/scrap/rework

* Delete as appropriate

Exercise 4.15   *Measurement test*

The multiple choice question paper will only be issued to candidates by their supervisor on satisfactory completion of the appropriate exercises. The answer sheet below must be completed by the candidate when the questions are issued.

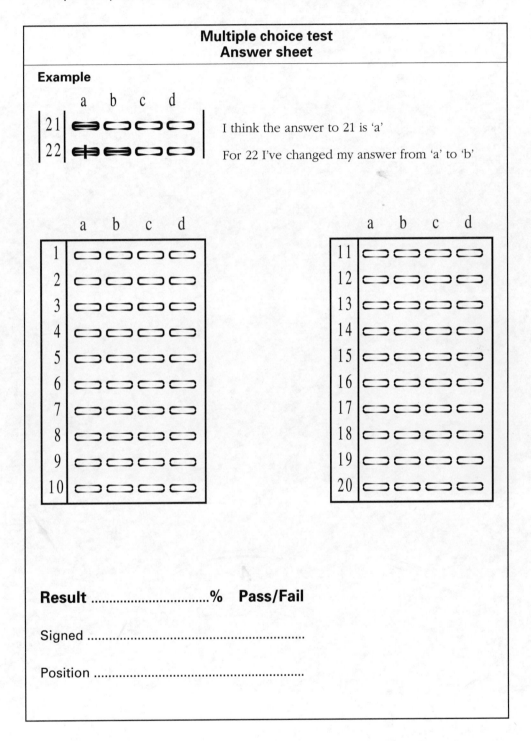

Chapter 5

Basic marking out

All information presented in this section is complete, accurate and legible		
All information presented in this section is in the format required		

A draughtsperson produces detailed drawings of components on paper. The engineering craftworker then proceeds with the manufacture of these components. Marking out is the process of marking guidelines onto the surface of the component material, the **workpiece**, before it is cut. These lines indicate the overall shape of the finished workpiece and mark the position of hole centres. Marking out is carried out by craftworkers before starting most jobs.

The first stage in marking out is to recognise the position of the datums on the drawing (see Chapter 3). Datums are the reference positions from which all measurements in each direction are taken. All the component's features should be marked out with reference to their datums. Drawings could have several datums, e.g. for height, for length and for width. For rectangular workpieces the datums for height and for length are usually two straight faces which are square (at 90°) to each other. For cylindrical and symmetrical work, the datum may be its centreline. Features on the end of a circular component frequently have a point as their datum.

Look at the drawings below and note that all the dimensions in each direction originate from either a face, a line or a point.

When marking out workpieces, the datum faces, lines or points are normally the same as those used on the drawing. Preparation of the datums on the workpiece is the initial stage in marking out. It must be carried out accurately as all subsequent lines are positioned relative to the datums. If using two face datums, they are usually prepared by filing them flat and square (at 90°) to each other. When using a line or a point datum, it must first be marked out onto the workpiece.

Once the datum has been established, the marking out of all other lines can then proceed using a variety of tools. Some of the most common marking-out tools are described in this chapter, together with their uses. For accuracy, marking-out tools must be of a high quality and must be carefully looked after.

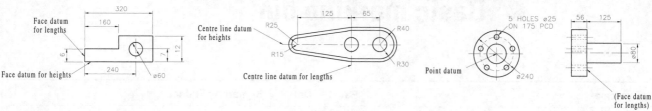

Face datum
Also known as edge datum or surface datum
Rectangular workpiece All lengths and
heights are dimensioned from two faces

Line datum
Symmetrical workpiece Height dimensioned
from the centreline of the workpiece Lengths
dimensioned from the centreline of the hole

Point datum
Circular workpiece
Features on the end face are
dimensioned from its centre point

Note: Face datums are often referred to as edge datums or surface datums.

Exercise 5.1   *Identification of datum positions on prepared drawings*

On the dimensioned drawings below, label datum faces with the letter F, datum lines with the letter L and datum points with the letter P. The first drawing has been completed for your guidance.

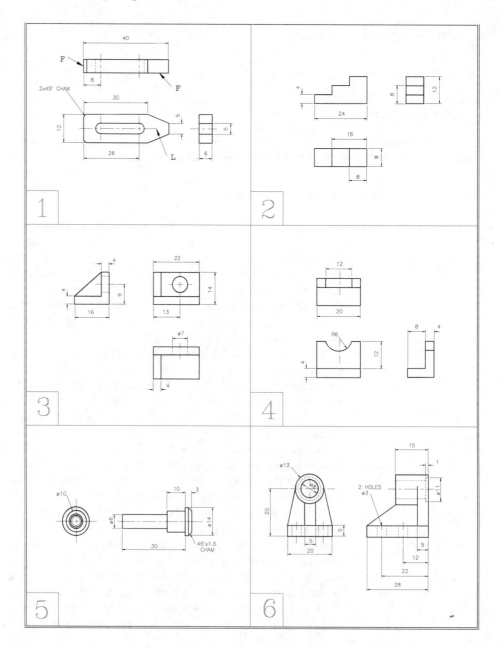

Pens and pencils

Pencils and pens are seldom used by engineers for marking out as they are not accurate enough. They leave a removable impression on the work and do not scratch the surface, so they are sometimes used to mark out materials where scratching is undesirable; for example:

- **Plated steel** – to avoid possible corrosion arising from scratching the protective coating.
- **Thin or fragile materials** – these could be damaged by scratching.
- **Components which are deliberately bent** – this avoids a possible weak point caused by scratching.

Scribers

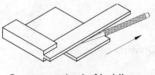

A typical engineer's scriber

Scribers are used by engineers together with guiding instruments such as rules, try squares, protractors and radius gauges for scribing (scratching) fine permanent lines onto the surface of the work. Scribers have a finely ground, hardened and tempered point which should be kept sharp; they are made from high carbon steel and are about 120 mm long. They are held in the same way as pens and have a knurled shank for grip.

When scribing lines, the scriber's point should fit between the guiding instrument and the work, as shown.

It is common practice to coat surfaces being marked out with a quick-drying blue dye or copper sulphate. This coating makes the scribed lines clear and easy to see as the scriber scratches the surface.

Safety note: Never carry scribers in your pockets; carry them with the point facing down.

Correct method of holding a scriber

Rules

Made from steel, an engineer's rule is a simple and easy tool to use for guiding a scriber when marking out straight lines. It is also used with a scriber for setting lengths. It has finely engraved divisions at 0.5 mm and 1/64 in spacing and can be used to this accuracy if care is taken. When marking out length with a rule and a scriber, ensure the rule is held at 90° to the work's datum face. The end of the rule is used to guide the scriber, as shown below.

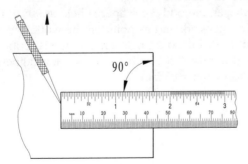

Correct method of marking out length with a rule

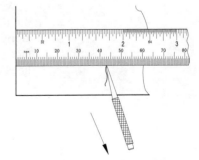

Incorrect method of marking out length with a rule: the scribed line will not be straight or square

Tape rules are longer than steel rules. They can be used for marking lengths on materials for which a steel rule is too short. Tape rules cannot be relied on for scribing straight lines as they are not rigid enough.

Care for your rule! The sides and ends of all rules should be protected from wear; they should not be used for turning, prising or cleaning anything, as this would damage the rule.

Radius gauges

To mark out an arc to a specific radius, a scriber can be used to scribe around a radius gauge. Care must be taken to ensure that the point of the scriber follows the profile of the radius gauge. An accuracy of about ±0.5 mm can be achieved if it is done very carefully. The procedure is not entirely satisfactory as it often results in limited precision. A preferred method of scribing arcs is to use dividers.

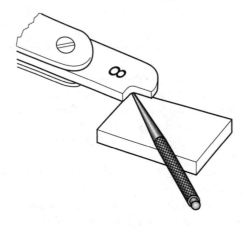

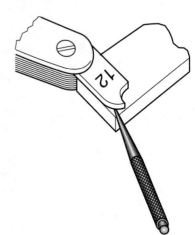

Drawing an internal radius

Drawing an external radius

Odd-leg calipers

Odd-leg calipers are also known as hermaphrodite or jenny calipers. Odd-leg calipers are used for scribing lines parallel to the datum face of a workpiece. The scribing leg of odd-leg calipers has a sharp point which is sometimes a replaceable piece. The other leg is shaped with a projecting heel or hook for locating on the work's datum face.

To set odd-leg calipers, the distance from the heel to the point is set with a rule. Note that the engraved lines on the rule enable the point of the odd legs to click into position to ensure an accurate setting.

When correctly set, the odd-leg caliper is held at 90° to the work, its heel against the datum face of the work and its point on the work. The odd-leg caliper is moved along the face of the work so a single straight line is scribed parallel to the work's face, as illustrated opposite. Set with a rule, odd-leg calipers can be used to mark out lines accurately to within ±0.5 mm.

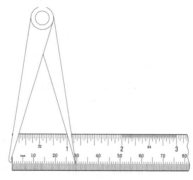

Setting odd-leg calipers on a rule

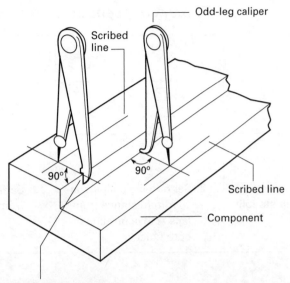

Odd-leg calipers used to scribe a line parallel to a datum face.
Note the two different heel types.

The lines scribed with odd leg calipers may represent the workpiece's outline or the centre line of a circle. The centre point of a circle is required for marking out circles, holes and radii. It is the point at which the two centre lines of the curved feature intersect. Centre points are frequently found by marking out two centrelines with odd-leg calipers.

Using odd-leg calipers to mark out centres

When marking out a hole or a radius, its centre point must first be located. The centre point is the intersection of the horizontal and vertical centre lines of the holes or radius. The illustrated component shows holes and a radius. The procedure for marking out their centre points is described below.

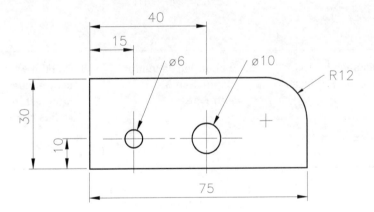

To mark out centres of two holes

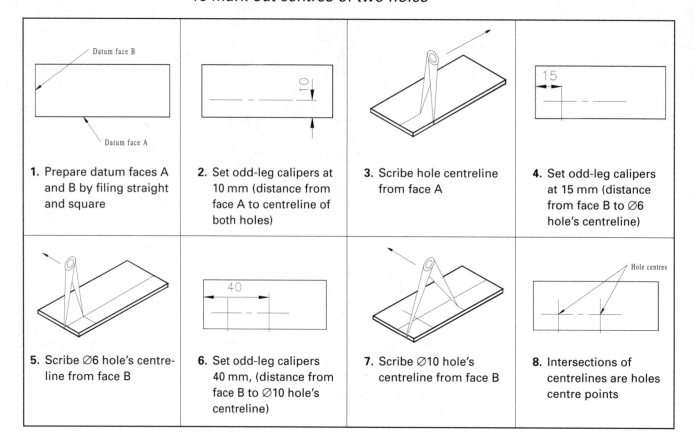

1. Prepare datum faces A and B by filing straight and square

2. Set odd-leg calipers at 10 mm (distance from face A to centreline of both holes)

3. Scribe hole centreline from face A

4. Set odd-leg calipers at 15 mm (distance from face B to Ø6 hole's centreline)

5. Scribe Ø6 hole's centre-line from face B

6. Set odd-leg calipers 40 mm, (distance from face B to Ø10 hole's centreline)

7. Scribe Ø10 hole's centreline from face B

8. Intersections of centrelines are holes centre points

To mark out centre of a radius

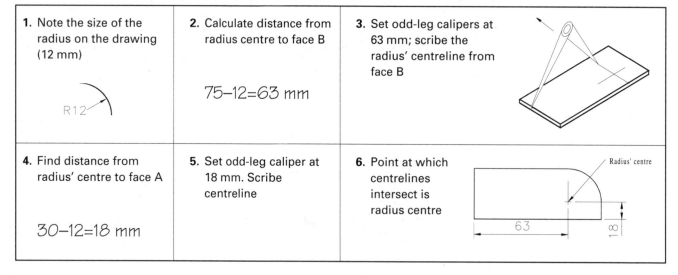

1. Note the size of the radius on the drawing (12 mm)

2. Calculate distance from radius centre to face B

$$75 - 12 = 63 \text{ mm}$$

3. Set odd-leg calipers at 63 mm; scribe the radius' centreline from face B

4. Find distance from radius' centre to face A

$$30 - 12 = 18 \text{ mm}$$

5. Set odd-leg caliper at 18 mm. Scribe centreline

6. Point at which centrelines intersect is radius centre

After the centre point has been accurately located, it can be punched and used for guiding a drill or for further marking-out procedures.

Dot punch and centre punch

Dot punches and centre punches are used to punch dimples during marking out. They are held vertically and lightly hit with a 1/2 lb (125 g) hammer. Each produces a different type of dimple but both are made of hardened and tempered 0.8% carbon steel. They are about 100 mm long and are knurled to give positive finger grip.

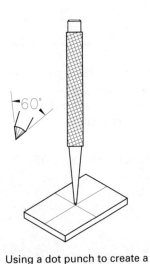

Using a dot punch to create a
dimple at a centre point

Dot punch

The **dot punch** has a 60° point and is used to:

- Punch dimples at the centre point of holes and radii for locating one of a divider's points when scribing circles and radii.
- Punch small equally spaced dimples along scribed lines at frequent intervals to enable the marked lines to be identified during cutting operations. Once cut, the remaining half of the dimple acts as a witness mark to show that the cutting operation has been performed accurately.

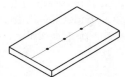

Small dimples equally spaced
along a scribed line

After cutting the workpiece, the
witness marks can still be seen

Dot punches are also used to punch dimples for marking out lengths with dividers.

A centre punch

Centre punch

The **centre punch** has a 90° point. It is used after a dot punch to increase the diameter of the dot-punched dimple. The larger dimple is to locate the point of a drill in position at the start of a drilling operation.

Centre punches are used as follows:

- To mark out a hole's centre point.
- To dot punch a *small* dimple at the centre point.
- To check the position of a dot-punched dimple.
- To repunch a dot-punched dimple.

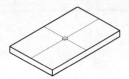

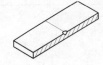

Centre-punched hole centre

Section through a centre-punched hole

Maintenance of scribers and punches

When sharpening centre punches and dot punches, hold the punch vertically against the grinding wheel at the appropriate angle. The grinding marks produced will lie away from the point and give the instrument a strong point. If the punch is held incorrectly and ground crossways, the point of the instrument is weakened.

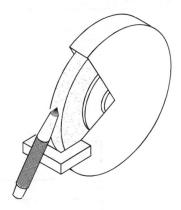

Correctly ground
point

Correct method of grinding the point:
the guard is not shown for clarity

Incorrectly ground
point

A pair of engineer's dividers

Dividers

Dividers are used to mark out circles, arcs and repeated pitches by scribing arcs. They are set to an accuracy of within ±0.5 mm on an engineer's rule. Each leg of the dividers has a sharp point and the instrument is held and turned by a peg on the bow.
    When marking out a circle with dividers, the procedure is as follows:

1. Mark out and dot punch the circle's centre point.
2. Set the distance between the divider points to the circle's radius with a rule (the divider points should click into one of the rule's engraved lines).
3. Locate one point of the divider legs into the dot-punched dimple.
4. Rotate the dividers by the peg to scribe a true circle.

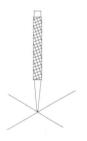

Dot punch circle's centre point

Set dividers at circle's radius

Locate one point in a dot-punched dimple

Scribe the circle

Using dividers to mark out a circle

Exercise 5.2   *Marking out a drill drift*

Follow the planned sequence of operations to mark out the drill drift illustrated below. Your lines should be clearly marked out within ±0.5 mm. Dot punch the outline at intervals of about 15–20 mm and at each intersection.

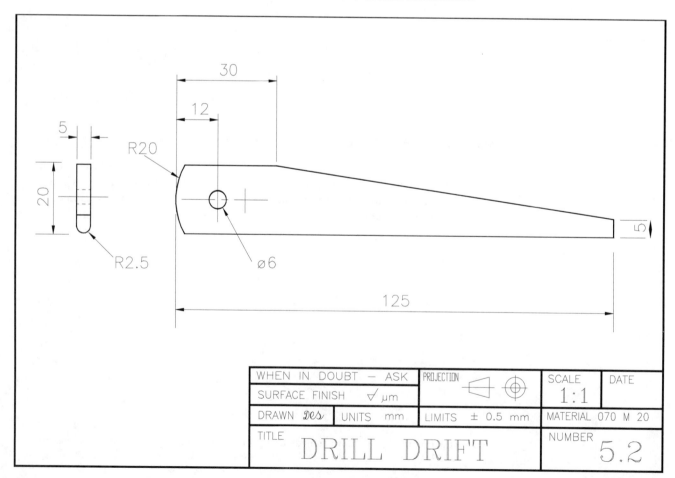

This plan is completed for your guidance. In future exercises you must plan the sequence of operations by completing similar tables *before* starting the marking out.

Task/line	Tools used
Prepare datum faces	File and try square
Mark out centreline	Odd-leg calipers and rule
Mark out 20 mm radius' centre	Odd-leg calipers and rule
Mark out Ø6mm hole centre	Odd-leg calipers and rule
Mark out overall length	Rule, scriber and try square
Mark out angled edge	Rule and scriber
Dot and centre punch centre points of hole and radius	Dot punch and $\frac{1}{2}$ lb hammer
Mark out radius and hole outline	Dividers and rule
Make all outlines more clear	Dot punch and $\frac{1}{2}$ lb hammer
Centre punch hole centre	Centre punch and $\frac{1}{2}$ lb hammer

Marking out equally spaced features

When a number of similar features are equally spaced along a line or around a circle, the distance between the features is called the pitch.

Linear pitches (straight line pitches)

To mark out six holes, equally spaced on a 60 mm line, the procedure is as follows.

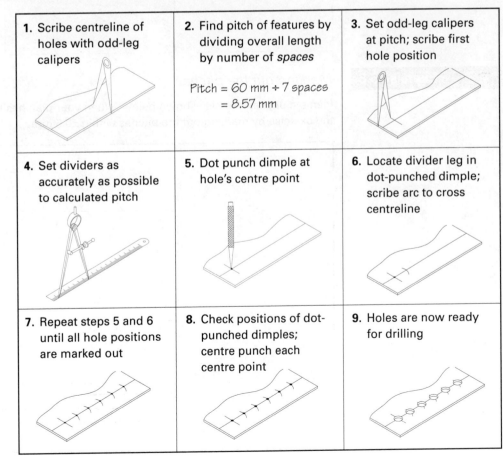

1. Scribe centreline of holes with odd-leg calipers	2. Find pitch of features by dividing overall length by number of *spaces* Pitch = 60 mm ÷ 7 spaces = 8.57 mm	3. Set odd-leg calipers at pitch; scribe first hole position
4. Set dividers as accurately as possible to calculated pitch	5. Dot punch dimple at hole's centre point	6. Locate divider leg in dot-punched dimple; scribe arc to cross centreline
7. Repeat steps 5 and 6 until all hole positions are marked out	8. Check positions of dot-punched dimples; centre punch each centre point	9. Holes are now ready for drilling

Pitch circle diameter (PCD)

When features are equally spaced on a circle, the circle is called a pitch circle diameter (PCD). To mark out eight equally spaced holes ready for drilling on a Ø60 mm PCD, the procedure is as follows.

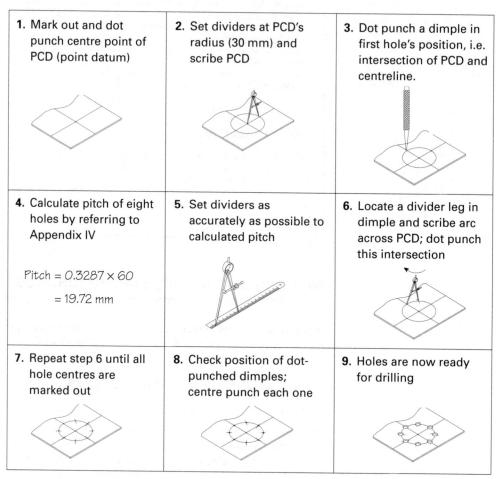

1. Mark out and dot punch centre point of PCD (point datum)	**2.** Set dividers at PCD's radius (30 mm) and scribe PCD	**3.** Dot punch a dimple in first hole's position, i.e. intersection of PCD and centreline.
4. Calculate pitch of eight holes by referring to Appendix IV Pitch = 0.3287 × 60 = 19.72 mm	**5.** Set dividers as accurately as possible to calculated pitch	**6.** Locate a divider leg in dimple and scribe arc across PCD; dot punch this intersection
7. Repeat step 6 until all hole centres are marked out	**8.** Check position of dot-punched dimples; centre punch each one	**9.** Holes are now ready for drilling

Exercise 5.3

Marking out the pitches

Plan the pitches exercise shown below. When your plan has been approved, complete the exercise by marking out the pitches within ±0.5 mm.

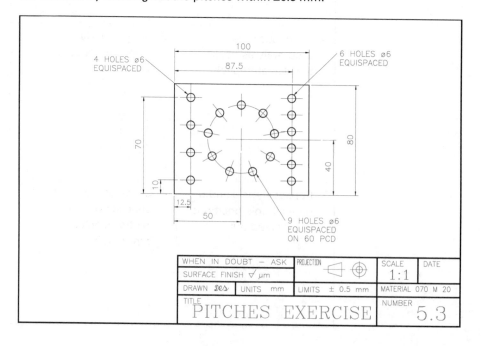

4 HOLES ø6 EQUISPACED

6 HOLES ø6 EQUISPACED

9 HOLES ø6 EQUISPACED ON 60 PCD

100
87.5
80
40
70
10
12.5
50

WHEN IN DOUBT — ASK	PROJECTION	SCALE	DATE
SURFACE FINISH √ µm		1:1	
DRAWN *Des*	UNITS mm	LIMITS ± 0.5 mm	MATERIAL 070 M 20

TITLE PITCHES EXERCISE

NUMBER 5.3

Planned sequence of operations for marking out the pitches

Task/line	Tools used

Centre square

Centre squares are used to mark out centre points at the ends of cylindrical bars. They can be supplied as part of a combination set or as specialist instruments.

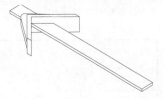

A combination set fitted with a centre head

The procedure to mark out a centre point at the end of a cylindrical bar is as follows.

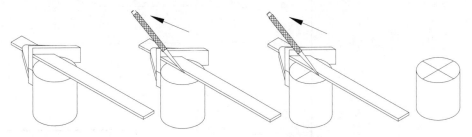

Locate centre square flat on end of bar, vee faces resting on bar's curved edge

Scribe line along straight edge (centreline of bar)

Rotate work 90° then scribe second centreline

Centre point at intersection of centre lines

Box square

A box square

A box square is a tool used to mark out lines on the side of a cylindrical workpiece parallel to the cylinder axis. Box squares are used for marking out keyways and slots. The procedure to mark out a slot on the side of a cylinder is as follows.

Hold box square against cylinder, scribe slot's centreline (datum)

Mark out the centre points for two 'circles' using odd-leg calipers; dot punch them carefully

Scribe 'circles' with dividers

Position box square on surface of cylinder; scribe line tangential to both 'circles'

Repeat step 4 on the other side of the slot

Completed marked-out slot

Exercise 5.4

Marking out the slotted tube

Plan the marking out of the slotted tube shown below using a box square and other necessary tools. When your plan has been approved, complete the exercise by marking it out within ±1/32 in.

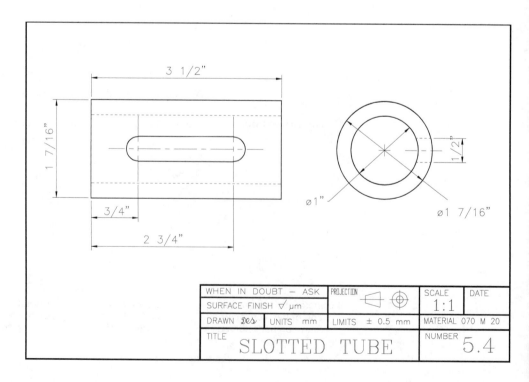

Planned sequence of operations for marking out the slotted tube

Task/line	Tools used

Surface plate

A surface plate provides a large flat reference surface for work and tools to rest on during marking out. The flat surface provides stability and enables the marking-out tools described in the following pages to be used efficiently. For easy access, surface plates are usually located on or near the workbench.

Surface plates are usually made of cast iron; it is self-lubricating and hard-wearing. Cast iron surface plates have ribs underneath which increase their rigidity.

In order to retain its flatness, a surface plate must be treated with extreme care:

- Always clean a surface plate with a soft dry cloth before use; oil and cover it after use.
- Always slide heavy objects onto a surface plate rather than lowering them.
- Do not drop anything onto a surface plate.
- Never hammer on a surface plate.

Surface plates can also be made from granite or glass. These materials are sometimes preferred as they are non-magnetic, rust-free and do not burr. All good quality surface plates are accurately finished conforming to BS 817 : 1988.

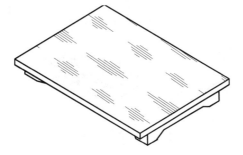

A cast iron surface plate with its protective cover removed

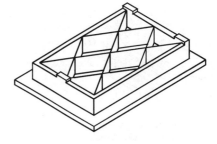

Underside of a cast iron surface plate showing its strengthening ribs

Angle plate

An angle plate is used to support a workpiece vertically on a surface plate so it can be marked out accurately. The work can be clamped to an angle plate when marking out from a line or point datum. Workpieces may be rested against an angle plate when marking out from a face datum.

Angle plates are made from cast iron in various designs. They are usually drilled or slotted so that bolts can go through them for clamping the workpiece. The surfaces of angle plates are accurately machined so they are square (at 90°) to one another.

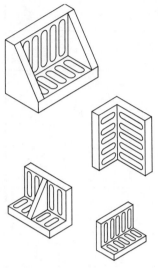

Three designs for a cast iron angle plate

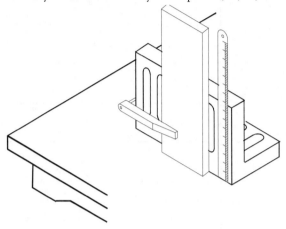

Work set up for marking out using an angle plate on a surface plate

Scribing blocks and surface gauges

A scribing block is used on a surface plate for marking out parallel lines on workpieces. Scribing blocks are made with a cast iron or hardened steel base and have a vertical steel spindle. A special double-ended scriber is clamped to the spindle so the height of the scriber's point can be set.

A scribing block is known as a surface gauge if it has a means of *fine* adjustment for setting the height of the scriber's point.

When marking out, the work and rule are set vertically against the angle plate. The height of the scriber's point is adjusted as required. The instrument is then moved along the surface plate, scribing a line on the workpiece as shown in the illustration.

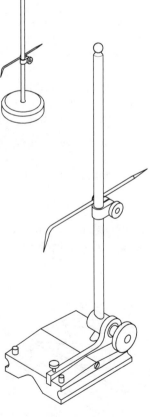

A surface gauge and a scribing block (inset)

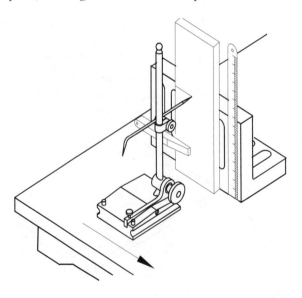

The usual method of setting out a surface gauge for marking out

Safety note: To avoid possible eye injury, wear safety glasses when using a surface gauge. The unused scribe point can be covered with a cork or rubber.

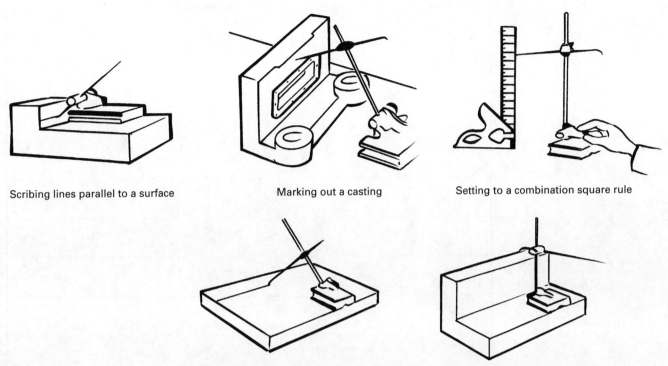

Scribing lines parallel to a surface | Marking out a casting | Setting to a combination square rule

Using the setting pins to scribe parallel to an edge | Checking a surface for parallelism

Some common methods of setting and using surface gauges

| **Exercise 5.5** | *Marking out the clamp rest* |

Plan the marking out of the clamp rest shown below using a surface gauge or scribing block. When your plan has been approved, complete the exercise by marking it out to within ±0.5 mm.

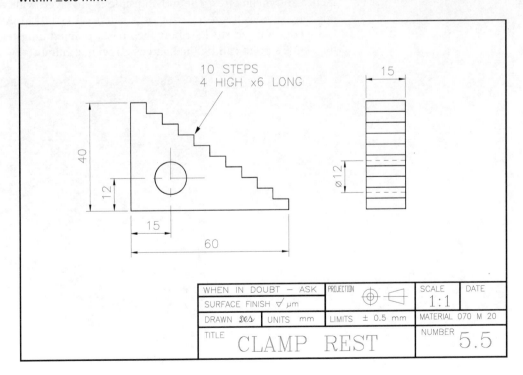

10 STEPS
4 HIGH x6 LONG

15

40

12

Ø 12

15

60

WHEN IN DOUBT — ASK	PROJECTION		SCALE 1:1	DATE
SURFACE FINISH √ μm				
DRAWN *DES*	UNITS mm	LIMITS ± 0.5 mm	MATERIAL 070 M 20	
TITLE CLAMP REST			NUMBER 5.5	

Planned sequence of operations for marking out the clamp rest

Task/line	Tools used

Vernier height gauge

Vernier height gauges are used to mark out lines onto workpieces very accurately. They have a large steel base for stability, and a hardened steel column engraved with inches and millimetres. The moving slide is engraved with vernier calibrations, enabling settings to an accuracy of 0.02 mm and 0.001 in. Attached to the moving slide is a wedge-shaped steel scribe which has a pointed tungsten carbide tip. The height of the scribe's point can be finely adjusted with a thumbscrew.

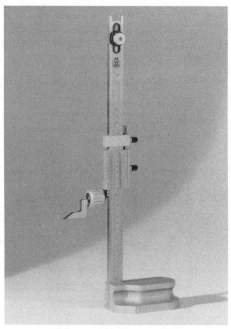

Vernier height gauge

The method of setting and reading a vernier height gauge is the same as for other vernier instruments, described in detail in Chapter 4.

The work to be marked out with a vernier height gauge must be set vertically on a surface plate using an angle plate.

The height of the scribe is set with the moving slide's fine adjusting screw. The marking out lines are then scribed onto the work surface by steadily moving the vernier height gauge along the surface plate (following the same procedure as with a surface gauge).

On the vernier height gauge shown, the height of the *main* scale can also be finely adjusted. This enables measurements to start from a convenient reading, which is useful if the shape of the workpiece requires it to be mounted on a parallel strip as shown below.

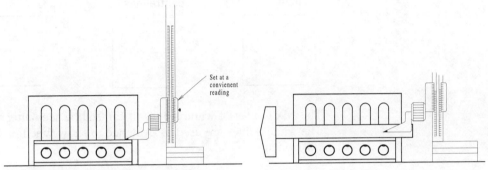

Set at a convenient reading

Set vernier height gauge at known height by touching on top of parallel bar and setting to a convenient reading

Mount work onto parallel bar and mark out all horizontal lines; remember to add height of the parallel to all settings

Work set on a parallel bar ready for marking out

Precision vernier height gauges must be stored in their original case and carefully used and maintained. If you suspect the instrument is inaccurate, it must be reported to your supervisor at the earliest opportunity.

Marking out circles with witness lines

When marking out large holes before drilling or boring operations, there are two common methods to show the machinist if the drill is running true or if it is slightly off-centre. These methods involve extra marking-out lines called witness lines. One of the following two procedures can be undertaken before drilling to mark out witness lines.

Concentric circles method

1. Mark out circle centrelines

2. Dot punch intersection of centre lines

3. Scribe required circle with dividers

4. Scribe a second, slightly larger circle

The second circle is a witness line. It can still be seen after the hole has been machined.

The witness lines are used as evidence to show whether the hole is accurately positioned.

Drill running true

Drill running below centre

Drill running to the left

Boxed circles method

This is another way of producing witness marks. These marks run parallel to the circle's centrelines and form a box around it.

1. Mark out centrelines of circle

2. Dot punch intersection of centrelines

3. Scribe required circle with dividers

4. Scribe lines tangential to circle forming a box

The box is a set of witness lines. It can still be seen after the hole has been machined. The witness lines are used as evidence to show whether the hole is accurately positioned.

Drill running true

Drill running below centre

Drill running to the left

Exercise 5.6

Marking out a depth-gauge body

Plan the marking out of the depth-gauge body below using a vernier height gauge and other necessary equipment. When your plan has been approved, mark it out within ±0.025 mm and box the circles.

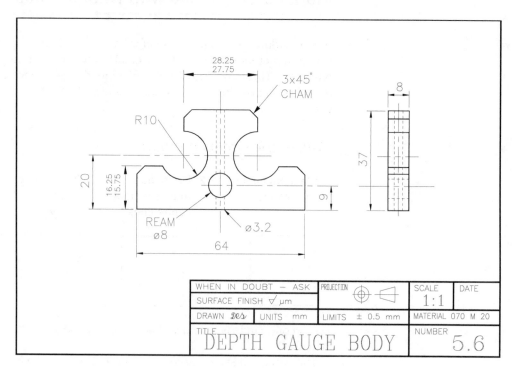

WHEN IN DOUBT — ASK	PROJECTION		SCALE 1:1	DATE
SURFACE FINISH ∇ µm				
DRAWN Des	UNITS mm	LIMITS ± 0.5 mm	MATERIAL 070 M 20	
TITLE DEPTH GAUGE BODY			NUMBER 5.6	

Planned sequence of operations for marking out the depth-gauge body

Task/line	Tools used

Workshop protractor

Workshop protractors can be used for marking out angles on workpieces. The reading and setting of workshop protractors is described in detail in Chapter 4. When marking out with a workshop protractor, an accuracy of about ±0.5° (called 30 arc minutes) can be readily achieved. A workshop protractor can be used as:

- a hand-held tool to guide a scriber
- a work-setting device on a surface plate

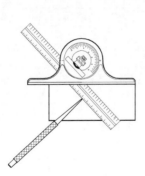

Using a workshop protractor
as a hand-held tool

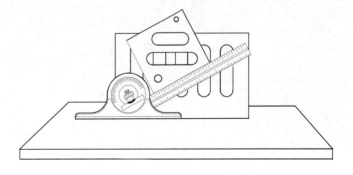

Using a workshop protractor
as a work-setting device

Vee blocks

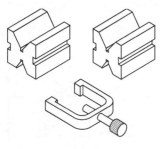

A pair of vee blocks
and their clamp

Vee blocks can be used for mounting cylindrical work (shafts) on surface plates, so the work can be accurately marked out on its sides or ends. They are also used to support rectangular work by one corner, so the work's sides are held at 45°. This enables lines to be accurately scribed on the work's surface at 45° with a surface gauge, scribing block or vernier height gauge.

Vee blocks have their surfaces accurately ground square to one another. There is a vee-shaped groove in at least one side into which the work is located. Made in either cast iron or case-hardened mild steel, vee blocks are usually supplied in matched pairs, often with a clamp so the work can be secured in position.

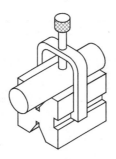

Work mounted longitudinally
on a vee block

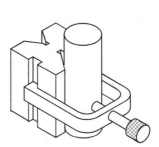

Work mounted vertically on
a vee block

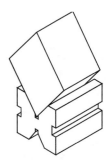

Vee block used to support
square-cornered work at 45°

Vee blocks can be used to mount shafts or cylindrical work for drilling. The shaft is mounted vertically for drilling along its axis, or horizontally for drilling across its axis.

Exercise 5.7

Marking out the angle-slotted plate

Plan the marking out of the angle-slotted plate below using the required tools and techniques. When your plan has been approved, complete the exercise by marking it out within ± 0.25 mm and ±1°.

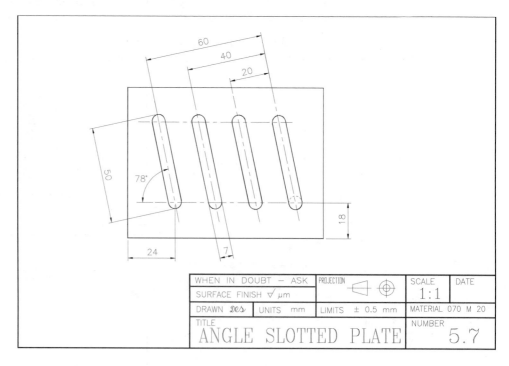

Planned sequence of operations for marking out the angle-slotted plate

Task/line	Tools used

Exercise 5.8 *Marking out test*

The multiple choice question paper will only be issued to candidates by their supervisor on satisfactory completion of the appropriate exercises. The answer sheet below must be completed by the candidate when the questions are issued.

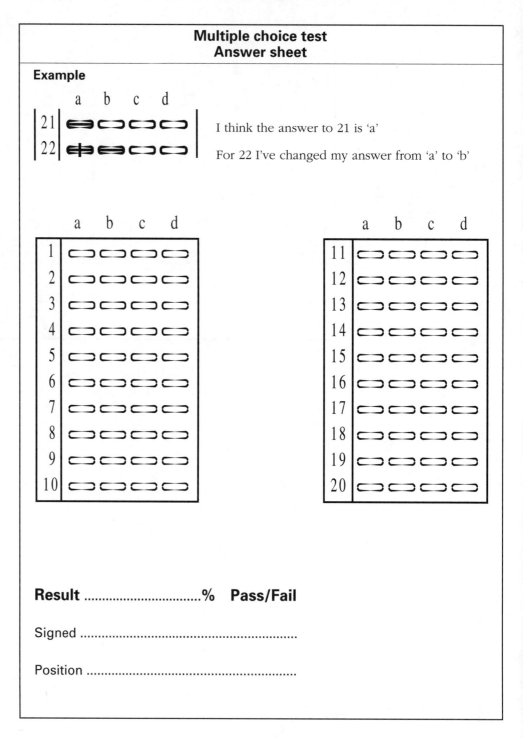

**Multiple choice test
Answer sheet**

Example

21 — I think the answer to 21 is 'a'

22 — For 22 I've changed my answer from 'a' to 'b'

Result ....% **Pass/Fail**

Signed ....

Position ....

Chapter 6

Basic engineering materials

Elements are the smallest particles of any substance that can be found. There are about 90 elements occurring naturally on earth and all materials are made from **elements**. A material that consists of only one element is said to be pure; however, most materials in their natural state are mixtures of many elements and are known as **raw materials**. These raw materials must be processed if they are to be of use in industry.

The processed materials of most interest to engineers are those which are reasonably plentiful and have properties suited to tooling and manufacturing. There are two basic types of material used extensively in engineering: **metals** and **non-metals**.

Metals

A metal is a raw material that is mined from the ground as an ore. After being solidified from the molten state, metals develop a crystalline structure and become good electrical conductors. Metals are not generally used in their pure state but are mixed together to form **alloys**. This mixing, or alloying, is to enhance certain properties or to make an alloy that is easier to work, i.e. to cut, bend or shape.

Metals can be divided into two categories: **ferrous** and **non-ferrous**. Ferrous metals and alloys contain the element iron. Steels are ferrous alloys made up of iron and small amounts of carbon and other elements.

Ferrous metals

Plain carbon steels

Plain carbon steels are the most versatile and widely used ferrous metals. They contain small amounts of manganese and are usually identified by their carbon content (0.1–1.5 per cent), see the table below.

Common name	Carbon (%)	Common uses
Mild Steel (or low carbon steel)	0.1–0.25	General-purpose, used throughout engineering
Medium carbon steel	0.25–0.7	Hammers and bolts, high stress components
High Carbon steel (or tool steel)	0.7–1.5	Metal cutting and forming tools

Mild steel
Sheet metal tool box

Medium carbon steel
Lifting hooks and chains

High carbon steel
Hand cutting tools

Cast iron

Cast iron is iron mixed with much larger amounts of carbon than the plain carbon steels. Grey cast iron is the most common type of cast iron and has a carbon content of 3.5 per cent together with other elements in small proportions. Cast iron is used because it is very fluid when molten; this enables large and intricate castings to be produced. Cast iron is quite brittle and has the quality of self-lubrication. Both these properties are caused by the excess carbon in its structure. Grey cast iron is used extensively for the production of premachined parts, e.g. motor-car engines and machine-tool frames. It is also used for marking out equipment, e.g. vee blocks and angle plates.

Cast iron
Pulley mounting bracket

Cast iron
Angle plate

Alloy steels

Alloy steels are steels that have larger amounts of other metals in their composition than cast iron or plain carbon steels. Alloy steels frequently contain such elements as chromium, nickel, molybdenum and vanadium. They are usually developed for special purposes; for example, stainless steel is particularly resistant to corrosion and is used in the food processing and chemical industries. High speed steel (HSS) is a special alloy steel developed for its hardness and toughness, and is used for the manufacture of metal-cutting tools, e.g. twist drills and milling cutters.

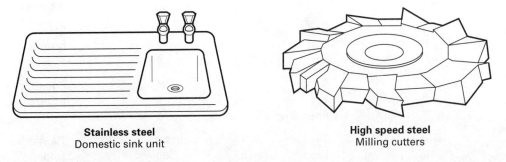

Stainless steel
Domestic sink unit

High speed steel
Milling cutters

Non-ferrous metals

Non-ferrous metals are metals and alloys that do not contain iron. Aluminium, copper, tin, lead and zinc are a few examples of non-ferrous metals. Each metal has its own properties and uses, and although copper is used for electrical wires and water pipes, non-ferrous metals are generally mixed together to form alloys. Many non-ferrous metals and alloys are corrosion resistant.

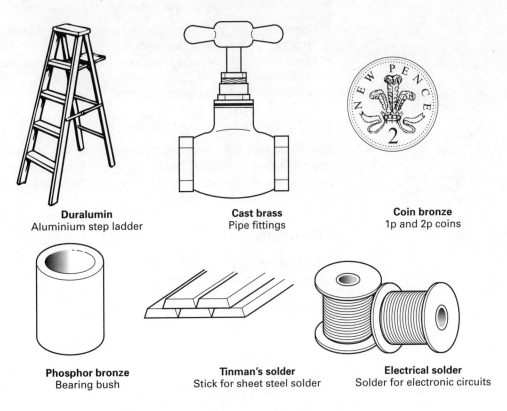

Duralumin
Aluminium step ladder

Cast brass
Pipe fittings

Coin bronze
1p and 2p coins

Phosphor bronze
Bearing bush

Tinman's solder
Stick for sheet steel solder

Electrical solder
Solder for electronic circuits

The table below shows the composition of some common non-ferrous alloys used in engineering.

Metals alloyed	Common composition (%)	Name of alloy
Aluminium	96	Duralumin
Copper	4	
Copper	40	Cast brass
Zinc	60	(Muntz metal)
Copper	96	Coin
Zinc	2.5	bronze
Tin	0.5	
Copper	94	Phosphor
Tin	5	bronze
Phosphorus	1	
Tin	40	Tinman's
Lead	60	solder
Tin	30	Electrical
Lead	70	solder

Percentages are approximate.

Non-metals

Non-metals are diverse in their make-up. They can be:

- **Organic** – derived from plants and animals, e.g. rubber and wood.
- **Mineral** – e.g. oils and stone.
- **Plastic** – the most common non-metals used in engineering, they tend to be:
  (a) lightweight
  (b) strong in relation to their weight
  (c) good insulators
  (d) resistant to corrosion from acids

Plastic materials have been synthetically made by processing organic and/or mineral materials. They have giant molecules which bond together in different ways to produce two distinct types of materials. The two types of plastics are recognised by how they behave when heated.

Thermoplastics

Thermoplastics are materials that are usually moulded while hot as they can be reshaped by heating. The molecular structure is long-chain or branched. Some common thermoplastics are Perspex, nylon, polyvinyl chloride (PVC), and polythene.
Some common uses for thermoplastic materials are illustrated below.

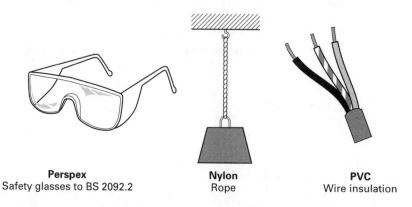

Perspex
Safety glasses to BS 2092.2

Nylon
Rope

PVC
Wire insulation

Thermosetting plastics

Thermosetting plastics are shaped by chemical action and harden on heating. Their molecular structure is **cross linked** which gives the material hardness and rigidity. Some common thermosetting plastics are epoxy resin, glass fibre and urea formaldehyde. Common uses for these hard and rigid materials are illustrated below.

| **Epoxy resin**
Adhesive | **Glass fibre**
Kit-car body | **Urea formaldehyde**
Electrical |

Identification of properties

The properties of materials, particularly metals, can be enhanced by alloying them, e.g. the addition of manganese into steel makes it easier to forge and roll. There are very few metals used in their pure state, most are alloyed with other elements to enhance the properties of the material or to make it easier to manufacture.

A designer chooses the material for a product and plans its manufacturing process. In order to do this, the designer must understand the properties of a wide range of materials.

Study the list of material properties below. Technical tests are available for most properties to enable accurate comparisons to be made; in this list *simple* workshop tests have been suggested where appropriate.

Exercise 6.1

Identification of properties of materials

Give a further example and indicate where and why each property discussed below is required.

Hardness   The degree to which a material can resist indentation, abrasion or scratching. Hard materials are difficult to cut either by sawing or filing, so these processes can be used as a simple test to compare different materials for hardness.

1   Metal-cutting tools need to be hard because they cut other metals.

2

Toughness   The degree to which a material can resist repeated hammering without permanently deforming. A simple toughness test can be devised by lightly hammering materials with the same force and seeing which deforms the most.

1   Hammer heads must be tough because they endure repeated blows.

2

Strength   The degree to which a material resists various forces without breaking. Three different types of strengths are listed below.

Tensile strength – The property of withstanding tensile (stretching) loads without breaking. A simple test is to try to bend the material; if it is hard to bend, it has tensile strength.

1   A bolt, when tightened is in tension, so it must exhibit tensile strength.

2

Compressive strength – The property of withstanding compression loads without crumbling or breaking.

1   Example 1   Building bricks need to withstand the weight of the wall above.

2   Example 2

Shear strength – The property of being able to resist being cut by a shearing action. A simple workshop test for shear strength is to try to cut pieces of different materials of the same thickness with tin snips, then to note which need the most force.

1   The hinge pin in a pair of scissors must be able to resist more shear force than the material being cut.

2

Ductility   The degree to which a material can be permanently stretched when subjected to a tensile force.

1   Wire drawing needs a ductile material, so it can be stretched into long fine lengths.

2

Conductivity   A good conductor will allow heat or electricity to pass through it. Most conductors allow both heat and electricity to pass through them.

1   Cooking pans need to allow the heat from the cooker to get to the food inside.

2

Malleability   The degree to which a material can be shaped by hammering or other compressive loading. A workshop test for malleability is to squeeze samples in a vice and examine them to see which has deformed the most.

1   Putty needs to be malleable to seal joints around house window frames because it is squeezed into the joint.

2

Corrosion resistance   Corrosion resistance is the prevention of the wearing away or dissolving of materials due to environmental factors. In order to prevent carbon steels from corroding, a coating is usually applied to the exposed surfaces. This coating may be paint, plate or just a smear of oil or grease. Where the material is exposed to greater risk, special materials may be used, e.g. stainless steel is used in food processing plant.

1   *Corrosion of motor-car bodies is prevented by the use of hard cellulose paints.*

2

Magnetism   Only three common elements exhibit the property of magnetism: iron, cobalt and nickel. A simple workshop test for a magnetic material is to see whether the material is attracted to a magnet. Also note that an electric current has a magnetic field around it. Copper is used as windings in electric motors because it is a good electrical conductor and can be made into a strong temporary magnet by having an electric current passed through it.

1   *Screwdriver points may be magnetic to enable steel screws to be positioned in difficult corners.*

2

Colour   All materials can be identified by colour. Colour can be used in several ways to identify materials:

- The outward appearance of the material changes from one material to another (gold and silver being the most obvious).
- The temperature of a metal can be estimated by its colour (steels are cherry red at 760 °C).
- The colour of sparks from a grinding operation depends on the type of material being ground (mild steel sparks are more yellow than high carbon steels).
- Different materials put into a naked flame change the colour of the flame (copper changes a flames colour to green).

1   *Coins need to be quickly and easily identified, so they are made from different-coloured metals.*

2

Brittleness   If a material is brittle, it will not deform on breaking. Brittle materials are easily identified after being broken because there is little or no deformation of the pieces and they can be reassembled (Brittleness is not normally considered a desirable property.)

1   *Glass and cast iron are both brittle; after breaking them the pieces can be reassembled.*

2

Comparison of properties

Exercise 6.2   *Comparison of material properties*

Take the samples of marked materials from the tool store and conduct tests on them to find the required properties in the table. Complete the table by scaling your results from 1 to 6 in the following way:

- For hardness write 1 for the hardest and 6 for the softest.
- For toughness, write 1 for the toughest and 6 for the least tough.
- For tensile strength, write 1 for the strongest and 6 for the least strong.
- For shear strength, write 1 for the strongest and 6 for the weakest.
- For malleability, write 1 for the most and 6 for the least malleable.

- For colour, write grey, silver, silver/grey, brown, golden/yellow or silver/white.
- For magnetism, insert either yes or no.

High carbon	Mild steel		Aluminium	Brass	Cast iron steel	Copper
Hardness						
Toughness						
Tensile strength						
Shear strength						
Malleability						
Colour						
Magnetism						

Recognition of materials

Exercise 6.3

Recognition of materials

Look around the workshop and find the material types listed in the table below. For each material, state:

- How recognised
- Application, i.e. what it is used for
- Reason for use, i.e. which properties make it suitable

The first row has been completed for your guidance.

Material	How recognised	Application	Reason for use
Duralumin (aluminium alloy)	Lightweight, silvery white in colour, free of corrosion.	Step ladder	Light weight, high strength.
Brass			
Cast iron			
Copper			
Mild steel			
Thermosetting plastic			
Thermoplastic			
Stainless steel			

Forms of supply

Raw materials can be supplied in many different forms. The choice allows companies to order their materials in a condition which will enable them to undertake their processing more efficiently. This results in savings to be made because the material is bought in the most appropriate form. It is therefore important to know and identify the forms in which materials can be supplied.

Exercise 6.4

Forms of supply for materials

For each of the forms of supply, draw a further diagram and state a use for your sketch.

Black rolled bar
Black bar is supplied in long rectangular, square or round sections which are not as smooth or as accurate as bright bar (see below). But it is cheaper to buy and is easier to cut, so black bar is usually selected when large amounts of machining are to be done.

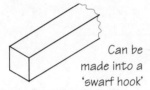

Can be made into a 'swarf hook'

Hot rolled sections
Often used for fabrications and in the construction industry, hot rolled sections are available in a wide variety of shapes and sizes: H, I and Channel sections are common. Angle bar is probably the most widely used hot rolled section but special sections can be bought, e.g. railway lines.

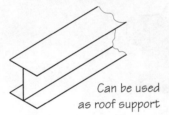

Can be used as roof support

Plate
Plate is the term used for pieces of hot rolled steels. Its surfaces are not smooth; it is 5–50 mm thick and up to 5 m wide. Plate is used in shipbuilding and boiler making.

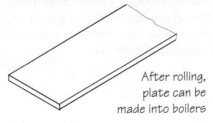

After rolling, plate can be made into boilers

Bright rolled bar
Bright bar, as it is commonly known, is smooth and accurate in its dimensions. It is supplied in long lengths of constant cross-section, usually square, rectangular or round. Bright bar is used if the external dimensions of the bar are similar to those of the finished product. It is not suitable for applications involving a lot of machining because it has internal stresses and is tougher than black bar (see above).

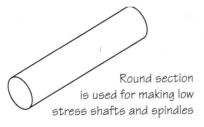

Round section is used for making low stress shafts and spindles

Sheet

Sheet is supplied in rectangular cut lengths to most companies; it is also available in coiled rolls for users of large amounts like the motor industry. Sheet has a smooth surface and can be bent, folded or pressed into a wide variety of products. Sheet is cold rolled, producing better dimensional accuracy and surface finish than plate. Although most sheet is supplied at around 1–2 mm thick, the thinnest mild steel sheet available is only 0.15 mm thick. For an extra charge, sheets can be supplied coated with zinc (galvanising), tin (tinplate) or plastic (Colourcoat) surfaces for corrosion resistance.

Rolled sheet is used for the production of motor-car bodies

Castings.

For intricate or complicated components it is common practice to purchase preformed cast blanks of the component, ready for finishing. Sandcasting is the most common method of manufacturing large iron items, whereas die casting is used for smaller non-ferrous components that need a smooth surface.

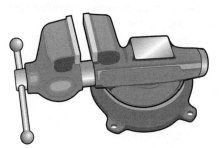

Used for vice frames (not jaws)

Forgings

A forged component has been shaped by hammering while hot. Forging is frequently selected as a manufacturing process because it produces components with an enhanced grain structure, resulting in greater toughness and strength. Forging is also a quick method of producing a complicated shape.

Used for chisels and other hand tools

Extrusions

Extrusion is to squeeze a material through a shaped hole. Toothpaste is extruded through the tube nozzle. Malleable metals and plastics can be extruded to make long strips of regular cross-section for applications such as greenhouse frames and uPVC window frames.

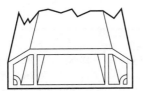

Used for decorative domestic
wire ducting

Mouldings

Moulding is the term used for some plastic shaping processes. Plastics can be die cast in a similar way to metals. As polymers become plastic when heated, plastic sheets can be shaped around a pattern with air pressure (or a vacuum) to form products with very thin walls, e.g. separators within a chocolate box, plastic bottles.

Used for many plastic products,
e.g. computer parts

Exercise 6.5   *Identification of forms of supply for materials*

Look around the workshop and find the products listed in the table below. For each product, state a reasonable form of supply to the manufacturer. Then state the reason why the selected form of supply was chosen for the product. The first row has been completed for your guidance.

Product	Form of supply	Reason for using this form of supply
Machine frame	Casting	Cast iron is rigid and strong
Steel rule		
Screwdriver handle		
Filing cabinet		
Aluminium ladder		
Vice jaw		
Socket screw head		
Surface plate		
Fabricated bench or table legs		
Pliers		

Defects in materials

On delivery, before any materials are accepted, it is good practice to visually examine the materials for defects. Some common defects are described below, together with some simple methods of detection (more sophisticated methods are mentioned where appropriate). The effect of the defect on the serviceability of the materials is also introduced.

Cracks

Cracks are common in heat treated components like this chisel

If bright, rolled steel bar contains excessive sulphur it is prone to cracking. Forged components can crack if they have been hammered while not hot enough. Cracking can also occur if a component has been cooled too quickly during heat treatment. Cracks weaken materials and should be avoided in all highly stressed components.

A reliable method of testing for cracks is to spray a penetrating die over the surface of the workpiece being tested. When the die has soaked into the surface of the component, it is wiped dry and a developer powder is dusted onto the component's surface. If a crack exists, the penetrating fluid is drawn out by the developer and shows as a stain. More reliable methods of crack detection are to use X-ray equipment or ultrasonic equipment.

Blowholes

Blowholes are large voids inside castings; they are caused by poor venting during manufacture. Blowholes cause weakness and are unsightly. Although they are invisible immediately after casting, a blowhole can become exposed during machining. The component would then be scrapped after time had been spent on it's manufacture.

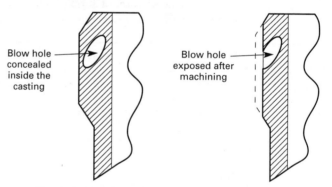

Blow hole concealed inside the casting

Blow hole exposed after machining

Blowholes are exposed when a casting is machined

To test for blowholes, samples of the casting can be sawn into pieces and visually inspected. If it is necessary to inspect all the components in a batch, X-ray or ultrasonic equipment would need to be used.

Distortion

If a component has been incorrectly quenched after heat treatment, or if it has been machined without first being stress relieved, it may become warped. Distorted components can be straightened, this is time-consuming and it might cause internal stress to develop in the component.

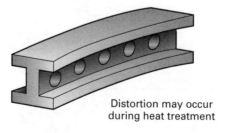

Distortion may occur during heat treatment

Distortion in bar stock can be detected by comparing the component surface with a straight edge or a flat reference surface.

Scale

Scale is the term used for hard areas on the surface of cast or forged components. Scale can appear as flakes, which are removed with a wire brush or file. If the scale is embedded in the skin of the component, it cannot be removed easily. Scale can conceal small surface cracks, it can also cause excessive wear on cutting tools.

Scale can easily be seen and should be removed with a wire brush, if at all possible, to expose any defects on the material's surface. In large steelworks, scale is removed with sulphuric acid.

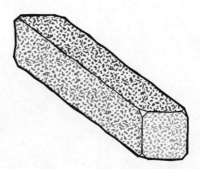

Loose scale should be removed with a wire brush

Exercise 6.6

Determination of the serviceability of defective materials

Note: For this exercise it would be beneficial to exchange your letters with a colleague doing the same exercise. In this case a copy of your letter would require.

Part A

From the list of possible material defects below, choose one defective material and write a letter offering to sell this defective material to a fictitious company. The company is producing one of the products listed in the customer's product range. Your letter should outline the defect and offer a generous percentage discount as an incentive to buy. It should also convince the prospective buyer that the material, although known to be faulty, will satisfy the intended purpose without significant manufacturing problems.

List of defective materials

- Cracks in wrought materials
- Scale in wrought materials
- Cracks in castings
- Blowholes in castings
- Distorted bar stock

Product range of your customer

Castings	Wrought materials	Bar stock
Cast iron gearbox cases	Forged steel connecting rods	Cylinder head studs
Cast aluminium pistons	Hot rolled steel girders	Steel tee nuts
Cast iron machine handwheels	Cold rolled car panels	Centre punches
Cast brass valve bodies	Welded iron garden gates	Gearbox shafts

Company & Co. Ltd   From:
Wherever
NVQ 24U   Date:

Dear Mr

Yours sincerely

Part B

You receive a letter from a company trying to encourage you to buy some defective materials at a discounted price. Write a reply, stating the reasons for accepting or rejecting the offer, giving good reasons how you think this would affect your companies reputation.

A. N. Engineering Company   From:
Elastic Industrial Estate
257 Short Street
Leeds   Date:

Dear Mr

Yours

En numbers and BS 970

During the second world war there was rapid movement in the development of steels. These new materials were given emergency numbers (En) for identification. In 1955 BS 970 was introduced to catalogue all materials. BS 970 was updated to enable easy identification of materials in 1983 and 1991; it is a four-part document and recommends specifications for wrought steels for mechanical and allied engineering purposes.

The section of most interest to general engineers is Part 1, which deals with inspection and testing procedures and specific requirements for carbon, carbon-manganese, alloy and stainless steels. The recommendation in BS 970 is to use a six-digit code to describe the steels specification The code is used as follows:

- The first three numbers represent the type of steel:

  000–199 *indicates a plain carbon steel*
  (the number is 100 times the manganese content)
  200–249 *indicates a free cutting carbon steel*
  (the number is 100 times the sulphur content)
  250 *indicates a particular type of silicon-manganese spring steel*
  251–299 *indicates a free-cutting alloy or stainless steel*
  300–499 *indicates a particular type of stainless or valve steel*
  500–999 *indicates a particular type of alloy steel*

- One of four letters follow:

  A for steel supplied to chemical composition requirements
  H for steel supplied to hardenability requirements
  M for steel supplied to mechanical property requirements
  S for a type of stainless steel

- The fifth and sixth numbers correspond to 100 times the amount of carbon in the steel.

An example of the BS 970 coding could be a steel of specification **BS 970 : 070 M 26**. This steel can be defined as follows:

- A manganese steel with 0.70% manganese content   (070 ÷ 100)
- Supplied on mechanical property specification   (Letter M)
- A carbon content of 0.26%.   (26 ÷ 100)

Exercise 6.7

Finding the composition of steels

[See also Exercise 7.2 Handling engineering information]

For the BS steel specifications listed in the table below, use BS 970 to find their material compositions. You may use any other source of information containing extracts from BS 970.

BS 970 specification	Material type	Description of material composition
080 M 50	Medium carbon steel	Contains 0.8% manganese, supplied on mechanical property specification, and 0.5% Carbon.
060 A 62		
606 M 36		
316 S 16		

Colour codes and abbreviations

Some steel suppliers paint a colour on steel bars to enable easy and quick identification. This code is not a BS recommendation for steels, so most companies use their own codes (see table below).

Draughtspersons may use any of the following abbreviations to describe a material. Most of the following abbreviations are not specific to a material but describe the material in loose or general terms:

MS = mild steel
BMS = bright mild steel
CI = cast iron
HCS = high carbon steel
Ally = aluminium alloy

Shown below is the BS 970 specification and old En equivalent of some steels, together with the colour code used by a leading UK steel stockholder.

Material type	New BS 970 : 1991 spec	Old BS 970 : 1955 (En) spec	Common colour code
Low carbon steel (or mild steel)	080 A 15	En3B (equivalent)	blue
	070 M 20	En3B	blue/red
	080 M15	En32B	red
Free-cutting steels	230 M 07	En1A	green
	230 M 07 (leaded)	En1A (leaded)	magenta
Medium carbon steel	080 M 40	En8	yellow
Alloy steels	605 M 36	En16	white
	708 M 40	En19	yellow/white
	817 M 40	En24	white/blue
	655 M 13	En36	white/red

Identification of materials

Exercise 6.7

Identification of materials

Take the box of eight unnamed material samples from the tool store. Examine and record each sample's properties in the table after conducting simple workshop tests and observations. From the information gained, you should be able to identify each of the material types. Listed in alphabetical order, the eight materials are:

- Aluminium
- Brass
- Bronze
- Cast iron
- Copper
- High carbon steel
- Mild steel
- Stainless steel

Sample	Material colour	Magnetic	Weight	Hardness	Material
1					
2					
3					
4					
5					
6					
7					
8					

Exercise 6.9   *Engineering materials test*

The multiple choice question paper will only be issued to candidates by their supervisor on satisfactory completion of the appropriate exercises. The answer sheet below must be completed by the candidate when the questions are issued.

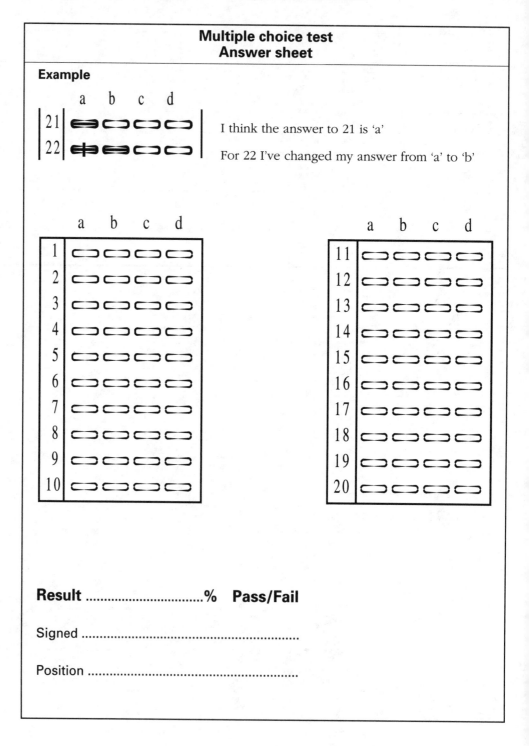

Chapter 7

Handling engineering information

Exercise*		Page	Date	Signed by Trainer
7.1	Selection of appropriate sources of information	132		
7.2	Selection and verification of information sources	133		
7.3	Extraction and interpretation of information	134		
7.4	Making up for information deficiencies	135		
7.5	Planning a sequence of operations	137		
7.6	Evaluating engineering information (tapping sizes)	137		
7.7	Evaluating engineering information (inspection)	138		
7.8	Handling engineering information test	140		
All information presented in this section is complete, accurate and legible				
All information presented in this section is in the format required				

* Some of these exercises are assessed in conjunction with exercises in other in sections of the book; they are cross-referenced appropriately.

Information sources

An important part of an engineer's job is to be resourceful by acquiring and referring to information that enables work to be carried out to the correct standards. There is a wide variety of information available to assist engineers, from engineering drawings of new products to maintenance manuals for the repair of existing equipment.

Handling engineering information refers to looking things up, finding things out and correctly applying this new knowledge to work. You will have already been doing this as part of your NVQ course, but this chapter will assist further to show you how to get the best use out of handling and dealing with engineering information.

As you work through this chapter, you will need to refer to various sources of information, some of which could be at your place of work, your college and in public libraries.

Listed below are sources of information frequently used by engineers.

Engineering drawings

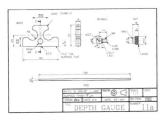

Engineering drawing

Engineering drawings are a common source of information showing the size, shape, material specifications of components, and illustrating how assemblies fit together. Methods of laying out and reading engineering drawings are explained in Chapter 3.

Written instructions

Written instructions

Clear written instructions provide a reference or a reminder of how to proceed, particularly useful for complicated tasks. By carefully following the written instructions for the exercises in this workbook you will complete the core units of the NVQ engineering course.

Information from personnel

Supervisors and other more experienced personnel will be able to deal with queries, answer questions and offer advice about work as well as issue instructions and information on how to do a particular task.

Verbal instructions

Reference books and booklets

A general encyclopaedia and dictionary can supply useful information. Engineering reference books include tables and charts, engineering formulae, health, safety and first aid.

Textbooks

Textbooks provide information on a wide variety of subjects and levels. If the description in the textbook is too complicated or inappropriate, remember there are lots of other textbooks to choose from.

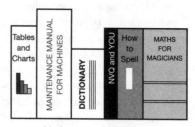

Various kinds of books

Maintenance manuals

Usually kept by the maintenance section, manuals show how parts are assembled and give their correct names. Correct part names are important when ordering replacements. Manuals provide information about service intervals, types of lubricant and instructions regarding maintenance and repair.

Mail

The post is a method of sending and receiving information.

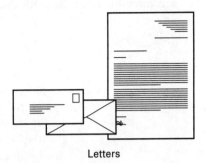

Letters

Publicity brochures and sales catalogues

Used for finding the availability, size, suitability and prices of tools and equipment, both nationally and internationally, they can be requested and supplied from most organisations and companies.

Publicity brochures

Counsellors, data sheets and wall charts

Free to customers, manufacturers often supply small pocket booklets (counsellors), data sheets and wall charts. They provide information about the use of various tools and equipment and include imperial–metric conversion tables.

A wall chart

Telephone

Telephone and fax

A quick way to request and receive information, telephones and faxes do need to be accompanied by a directory.

British Standards kitemark

BSI publications

BSI publications offer the most reliable source of detailed information on recommended standards for quality. Some British Standards relating to engineering are:

BS 308 Engineering drawing practice
BS 499 Welding terms and symbols
BS 970 Specification of wrought steels
BS 1134 Method for the assessment of surface texture
BS 1553 Graphical symbols for general engineering
BS 3643 ISO metric screw threads
*BS 3939 Graphical symbols for electrical power,
telecommunications and electronics diagrams*

CD-ROMs and computers

Engineering sales catalogues are becoming increasingly available on CD-ROM. They are popular with customers now offering up-to-date information and quick access.

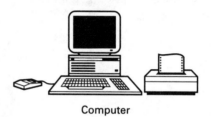

Computer

Signs

Many packages carry signs to show how they should be handled. Always read them; signs are there to protect both you and the contents of the package. Signs are also used to give information, instructions or warnings about work practices or the environment (see Chapter 1).

Instructions

Labels

Machines are often fitted with an identification number which should be quoted when reporting a fault or breakdown. Labels can be fitted to equipment, e.g. a label fitted to a chain may show its safe working load (SWL).

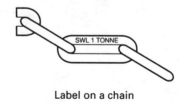

Label on a chain

Appendices

An appendix is a further source of information. The appendices to this book may prove helpful when completing some of the exercises in this chapter.

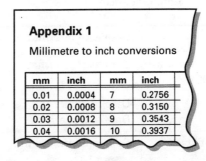

Appendix 1

Millimetre to inch conversions

mm	inch	mm	inch
0.01	0.0004	7	0.2756
0.02	0.0008	8	0.3150
0.03	0.0012	9	0.3543
0.04	0.0016	10	0.3937

Appendix

Selecting appropriate sources

It takes practice to find, select and use the most relevant and appropriate information for your requirements, i.e. the most useful information. Information should satisfy these criteria:

- **Clear** – Logical and straightforward to understand; if it isn't, try other information.

- **Suitable** – Choose a source of information best suited to what you want. For practical tasks, it may be more appropriate to ask an experienced colleague rather than looking at the instruction manual only. When looking for information about tools and equipment, don't just look in the sales catalogues, they will merely give you the information they want you to know, study specific engineering textbooks as well.

- **Relevant** – The information you find must be relevant and give the information needed. For example, it's no good looking up information about BS 970 codes for wrought steels when you need to find a particular steel's cutting speed. You should look in the appropriate toolmaker's counsellor. Remember to home in on what you need; do not be distracted by other information, even if it is interesting; return to it later when time permits.

- **Understood** – Repeat instructions to the person issuing them to make sure they know you have heard and understood them. Check you understand written information, study it carefully and ask your supervisor for advice if necessary.

- **Up to date** – Information is updated from time to time because specifications, standards, sizes and prices may change, so make sure the information you are going to use is up to date before starting work.

- **Reliable** – You must be confident that information is from a reliable source and correct. For example, when following instructions that have obviously been translated from a foreign language, you may need to rely on additional information with which you are familiar. And if you are referring to undated information, also perhaps unsigned or on unlabelled bits of paper, you should check its validity with a reliable source, usually your supervisor.

| Exercise 7.1 | *Selection of appropriate sources of information* |

For each of the information requirements, complete the table below by selecting an appropriate and relevant source of information. The first row has been completed for your guidance.

Information required	Details of information source
The total stopping distance for a motor car travelling at 50 mph	Source of information *The outside back cover of the Highway Code* Date of expiry *N/A* Date of issue *1993*
The colour used to identify the live wire on a 13 A plug	Source if information Date of expiry Date of issue
The recommended mileage between oil changes for a 1996 Ford Escort 1.6 L	Source if information Date of expiry Date of issue
The pitch of a 14 mm motor vehicle spark-plug thread	Source if information Date of expiry Date of issue
The percentages of metals contained in the alloy pewter	Source if information Date of expiry Date of issue
The price of 100 m of 1 mm^2 three-core flat with earth electrical cable	Source of information Location of supply Price valid until

Checking information is correct

Engineers rely on information, instructions and advice from various sources in order to do their work. Nobody, no matter how experienced, knows all there is to know about engineering. Therefore, considering the potentially hazardous work and environment, it is very important to check the source of information you depend on is:

- Correct, i.e. valid
- Applicable, i.e. appropriate or suitable for the task in hand

Information and instructions given to you by your supervisor should be correct; however, for your own benefit, consider anything anybody gives you. If you are uncertain, *ask*. If you are finding something out for yourself, you should check to make sure the information is correct and that it is applicable to what you have to do. There are several ways of verifying (checking) information, some of which are listed below:

- Ask the supervisor for verification or confirmation of the information you have.
- Refer to a manual, book or other data to check verbal information.
- Look for an expiry date or issue number if more than one version of the information is available.

- Confirm with the supplier by telephone, fax or letter before ordering anything to check specifications and prices; they can change without notice.
- When making a new component following written instructions, compare the component you are making with an existing component to check that your interpretation of the instructions is correct.
- Refer to British Standard or other approved registered information if you are unsure about symbols, abbreviations and standards.
- Ensure the information is relevant to the machine or equipment you are using by referring to the model number or machine type in the handbook.
- Telephone or fax the source of the information.
- Look and think; ask yourself, does it seem right?

Examples of verifying information:

- Alan needed a new vernier caliper within two weeks. He intended to order it through the catalogue, so he telephoned the catalogue company to confirm the vernier caliper's price and specifications (size, accuracy and range) were still as quoted there. And before placing the order, he also checked the supplier could guarantee delivery within two weeks.
- When Damon looked up the recommended cutting speed to drill a hole, he realised the cutting fluid specified for the material was not available on the machine he was using. Therefore he checked with his supervisor to confirm he could use a slower spindle speed on the machine for which there was cutting fluid available.

Exercise 7.2   *Selection and verification of information sources*

[This exercise cross-references with exercises in other chapters]

Complete the table below when doing the following exercises:

- Exercise 1.3: Identification of warning signs for groups of hazardous substances
- Exercise 3.7: Identification of BS 308 drawing conventions
- Exercise 3.8: Identification of BS 308 drawing abbreviations
- Exercise 6.7: Finding the composition of steels

Exercise reference	Information source	How verified
1.3	Title Author (or publication) Date of issue	
3.7	Title Author (or publication) Date of issue	
3.8	Title Author (or publication) Date of issue	
6.7	Title Author (or publication) Date of issue	

Using information

Having found an applicable source of information, the next step is to extract (take) and use the information required. Care must be taken when interpreting and using the information accurately; a mistake at this stage could cause problems later. Examples of what you may need to do are:

- Read tables, e.g. metric equivalent conversion tables.
- Follow text in books, e.g. instruction manuals.
- Be conversant with abbreviations used in your workplace, e.g. on written work instructions or on engineering drawings.
- Understand charts, e.g. BS 970 material specification.
- Understand information given on engineering drawings.
- Understand limit systems for tolerances on engineering drawings.

It is possible that you have been reading tables and charts as part of your daily training routine; if so, you will be familiar with them and know where they are located. For example, you probably read engineering drawings and conversion tables while at work, and you may read bus timetables to get to work.

| Exercise 7.3 | *Extraction and interpretation of information* |

Use the appendix of this book and any other appropriate sources of information which may be required to complete the exercises below. Your information must be recorded accurately. The first row has been completed for your guidance.

Exercise	Answer	Information source
Imperial (inch) equivalent to 34.86 mm	1.3725 in	Appendix I
Metric equivalent to 1.023 in		
Nearest millimetre drill size to 13/64 in available at your workplace		
BS specification code for the material that the pulley mount in Appendix V is made from		
Size limits of bored hole in boss of slideway shown in Appendix VI		
Pitch of six ∅8 holes on slideway shown in Appendix VI (use Appendix IV as reference)		
Current price of a 150 mm stainless steel engineer's rule with satin chrome finish		
Current price of 150 mm vernier caliper to measure internal and external depths and step lengths to within 0.02 mm		
Sketch British Standard (BS) electrical symbol for an electric clock		
Sketch British Standard (BS) symbol for a welded fillet joint		

Information deficiencies

When working from drawings or from written information, you may sometimes find that the information appears to be deficient, i.e. there seem to be bits missing. When this is the case, it's best to look again and check to make sure *you* haven't made a mistake.

If there is a deficiency in the information, it may be a genuine omission in the information, or it could be that the missing information is routine to the persons doing the job regularly and what you are looking for would not normally be shown.

After thoroughly checking the information, if you still think there are deficiencies in the information, look at an alternative source to make up for the deficiency. When you've found the missing information, ask your supervisor to check it. Here is an example of an information deficiency.

When making specified holes in components, it's best to know what they are for, i.e. their application, so the holes and their upper surfaces can be made to suit accordingly. Thread and hole specification were introduced in Chapter 3, where you should have noticed four hole types. Although each type has its own application, there isn't any information in this book about these applications, or indeed when each type would be appropriate; this is an information deficiency.

| Exercise 7.4 | *Making up for information deficiencies* |

Find an application and a reason for the use of each hole type shown below, then complete the table.

Spotfaced hole	Typical application for a spotfaced hole	Reason for using spotfaced holes

Titles of information sources used	Date of publication	Author/publication	Page

Reamed hole	Typical application for a reamed hole	Reason for using reamed holes

Titles of information sources used	Date of publication	Author/publication	Page

(Continued)

Counterbored hole	Typical application for a counterbored hole		Reason for using counterbored holes

Titles of information sources used	Date of publication	Author/publication	Page

Counter sunk hole	Typical application for a countersunk hole		Reason for using countersunk holes

Titles of information sources used	Date of publication	Author/publication	Page

Evaluating engineering information

Before acting on engineering information, you must fully assess and interpret it; this is known as evaluation. Already you will have been evaluating information to a greater or lesser extent. And it's well worth spending time to consider a proper evaluation of what the information actually means and how it can be best applied. Only then can a decision be made about how to proceed. Never be hasty and don't risk jumping to wrong conclusions; in the long run more time will be wasted.

Example 1

Planning sequences of operation

When given instructions to do a job, e.g. practical exercises in this book or making workpieces, it's best to plan a sequence of operations before starting. A sequence of operations is a plan of the order in which a job is to be carried out.

Exercise 5.2 considers the planned sequence of operations for marking out a drill drift. Decisions based on evaluations are outlined below:

- **Evaluations** – Reading and interpreting engineering drawings; assessing the safety equipment required to do the marking out
- **Decision making** – Selection of appropriate tools; selection of equipment; planning the sequence of operations to complete the work

| Exercise 7.5 | *Planning a sequence of operations* |

When you have planned the sequence of operations of *three* separate jobs from instructions, show these written plans to your supervisor for approval and signature. The sequence of operations shown to your supervisor may include those you have already done for exercises in other sections of this book.

The three planned sequences of operations presented as evidence by the trainee for assessment demonstrate that instructions have been correctly evaluated and the conclusions and decisions reached are valid and appropriate.

Verified by supervisor...

| Example 2 | *Tapping size tables and charts* |

When a threaded hole is specified, the hole must be predrilled before the thread-cutting process (tapping) can be done. To select the correct drill size (tapping size), engineers first read the thread size and pitch from the drawing. Reference is then made to a tapping table or chart to select the correct tapping size for the specified thread.

- **Evaluations** – Referring to engineering drawing; reading the thread size and pitch; referring to and reading the tapping size table or chart
- **Decision making** – Deciding on the correct drill size

| Exercise 7.6 | *Evaluating engineering information (tapping sizes)* |

Complete the exercise below by referring to a tapping size table or chart. Appendix III of this book can be used for some of the threads; however, others in the exercise are not listed in Appendix III as they are not in common use.

Source of information ....

Thread	Tapping size (mm drill size)	Thread	Pitch (tpi)	Tapping size (mm drill size)
M8 × 1.25 (metric coarse)		3/4 in UNC		
M10 × 1.25 (metric fine)		1 in UNF		
M12 × 1.25 (metric fine)		2 BA		
M24 × 3 (metric coarse)		4 BA		

Decisions and conclusions based on evaluating information should also be made *after* work has been completed as well as in its planning and production stage. This evaluation of completed work is most evident in the checking and inspection procedures to ensure satisfactory standards. Although many organisations have their own inspection procedures, initially an engineer would inspect his or her own work.

Example 3 *Checking and inspecting a finished workpiece*

[The workpiece may be a machined component, a welded assembly or an electrical/ electronic circuit]

After completing *any* work, it should be checked with the drawing specifications and instructions, and if appropriate it should be examined to see whether it functions correctly. When the work is considered satisfactory, it may then be approved by the supervisor and/or sent to the inspection department.

- **Evaluations** – Comparison of the finished workpiece with the permissible specification on the drawing or instructions
- **Decision making** – Selection of suitable tools for testing and measuring the workpiece; deciding whether the workpiece is acceptable, scrap or whether errors can be rectified

Exercise 7.7 *Evaluating engineering information (inspection)*

When you have carried out checks on any *two* finished workpieces, complete an initial inspection form for each. You may use the initial inspection forms below or your organisation's equivalent. Present the completed forms to your supervisor for approval and signature. It is not necessary to find an accurate workpiece for this exercise.

Initial inspection form			
Job title			
Job number	**Date**		**Checked by**
Component dimension	Limits of size	Actual size	Error
1			
2			
3			
Recommendations/decisions			

Initial inspection form			
Job title			
Job number	**Date**		**Checked by**
Component dimension	Limits of size	Actual size	Error
1			
2			
3			
4			
5			
6			
7			
Recommendations/decisions			

The two initial inspection forms presented as evidence for assessment demonstrate that the trainee has evaluated the information correctly and the decisions reached are valid and appropriate.

Verified by supervisor..

Exercise 7.8 *Handling engineering information test*

The multiple choice question paper will only be issued to candidates by their supervisor on satisfactory completion of the appropriate exercises. The answer sheet below must be completed by the candidate when the questions are issued.

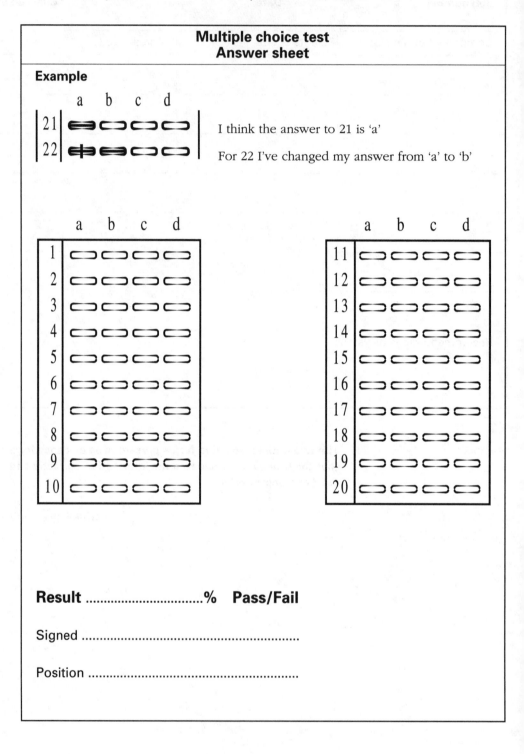

Millimetre to inch conversions

mm	inch	mm	inch	mm	inch	mm	inch	mm	inch
0.01	0.0004	7	0.2756	31	1.2205	55	2.1654	79	3.1102
0.02	0.0008	8	0.3150	32	1.2598	56	2.2047	80	3.1496
0.03	0.0012	9	0.3543	33	1.2992	57	2.2441	81	3.1890
0.04	0.0016	10	0.3937	34	1.3386	58	2.2835	82	3.2283
0.05	0.0020	11	0.4331	35	1.3780	59	2.3228	83	3.2677
0.06	0.0024	12	0.4724	36	1.4173	60	2.3622	84	3.3071
0.07	0.0028	13	0.5118	37	1.4567	61	2.4016	85	3.3465
0.08	0.0032	14	0.5512	38	1.4961	62	2.4409	86	3.3858
0.09	0.0035	15	0.5906	39	1.5354	63	2.4803	87	3.4252
0.1	0.0039	16	0.6299	40	1.5748	64	2.5197	88	3.4646
0.2	0.0079	17	0.6693	41	1.6142	65	2.5591	89	3.5039
0.3	0.0118	18	0.7087	42	1.6535	66	2.5984	90	3.5433
0.4	0.0158	19	0.7480	43	1.6929	67	2.6378	91	3.5827
0.5	0.0197	20	0.7874	44	1.7323	68	2.6772	92	3.6220
0.6	0.0236	21	0.8268	45	1.7717	69	2.7165	93	3.6614
0.7	0.0276	22	0.8661	46	1.8110	70	2.7559	94	3.7008
0.8	0.0315	23	0.9055	47	1.8504	71	2.7953	95	3.7402
0.9	0.0354	24	0.9559	48	1.8898	72	2.8346	96	3.7795
1	0.0394	25	0.9843	49	1.9291	73	2.8740	97	3.8189
2	0.0787	26	1.0236	50	1.9685	74	2.9134	98	3.8583
3	0.1181	27	1.0630	51	2.0079	75	2.9528	99	3.8976
4	0.1575	28	1.1024	52	2.0472	76	2.9921	100	3.9370
5	0.1969	29	1.1417	53	2.0866	77	3.0315	250	9.8430
6	0.2362	30	1.1811	54	2.1260	78	3.0709	1000	39.370

Example *To find the inch equivalent of 27.56 mm*

0.06 mm = 0.0024 in
0.5 mm = 0.0197 in
27 mm = 1.0630 in
Total = 1.0851 in

Inch to millimetre conversions

Fractional inch	Decimal inch	mm	Fractional inch	Decimal inch	mm	Fractional inch	Decimal inch	mm
–	0.001	0.0254	–	0.2	5.080	5/8	0.6250	15.88
–	0.002	0.0508	13/64	0.2031	5.16	41/64	0.6406	16.27
–	0.003	0.0762	7/32	0.2188	5.56	21/32	0.6562	16.67
–	0.004	0.1016	15/64	0.2344	5.95	43/64	0.6719	17.07
–	0.005	0.1270	1/4	0.2500	6.35	11/16	0.6875	17.46
–	0.006	0.1524	17/64	0.2656	6.75	–	0.7	17.780
–	0.007	0.1778	9/32	0.2813	7.14	45/64	0.7031	17.86
–	0.008	0.2032	19/64	0.2969	7.54	23/32	0.7188	18.26
–	0.009	0.2286	–	0.3	7.620	47/64	0.7344	18.65
–	0.01	0.254	5/16	0.3125	7.94	3/4	0.7500	19.05
1/64	0.0156	0.39	21/64	0.3281	8.33	49/64	0.7656	19.45
–	0.02	0.508	11/32	0.3438	8.73	25/32	0.7813	19.84
–	0.03	0.762	23/64	0.3594	9.13	51/64	0.7969	20.24
1/32	0.0312	0.79	3/8	0.3750	9.53	–	0.8	20.320
–	0.04	1.016	25/64	0.3906	9.92	13/16	0.8125	20.64
3/64	0.0469	1.19	–	0.4	10.160	53/64	0.8281	21.03
–	0.05	1.270	13/32	0.4063	10.32	27/32	0.8438	21.43
–	0.06	1.524	27/64	0.4219	10.72	55/64	0.8594	21.83
1/16	0.0625	1.59	7/16	0.4375	11.11	7/8	0.8750	22.23
	0.07	1.778	29/64	0.4531	11.51	57/64	0.8906	22.62
5/64	0.0781	1.98	15/32	0.4688	11.90	–	0.9	22.860
–	0.08	2.032	31/64	0.4844	12.30	29/32	0.9063	23.02
–	0.09	2.286	1/2 (0.5)	0.5000	12.70	59/64	0.9219	24.42
3/32	0.0938	2.38	33/64	0.5156	13.10	15/16	0.9375	23.81
–	0.1	2.540	17/32	0.5312	13.49	61/64	0.9531	24.21
7/64	0.1093	2.78	35/64	0.5469	13.89	31/32	0.9688	24.61
1/8	0.1250	3.18	9/16	0.5625	14.29	63/64	0.9844	25.00
9/64	0.1406	3.57	37/64	0.5781	14.68	1	1.0000	25.40
5/32	0.1563	3.97	19/32	0.5938	15.08	2	2.0000	50.80
11/64	0.1719	4.37	–	0.6	15.240	5	5.0000	127.00
3/16	0.1875	4.76	39/64	0.6094	15.48	10	10.000	254.00

Tapping sizes for common threads

The tapping sizes in this chart are for standard threads only

ISO Metric Thread angle 60°			BSW (Whitworth) Thread angle 55°			BSF (British Standard Fine) Thread angle 55°		
Major dia.	Pitch (mm)	Tapping size (mm)	Major dia (in)	Pitch (tpi)	Tapping size (mm)	Major dia.	Pitch (tpi)	Tapping size (mm)
M4 × 0.7		3.3	1/8	40	2.55	-	-	-
M5 × 0.8		4.2	3/16	24	3.7	3/16	32	4.0
M6 × 1.0		5.0	1/4	20	5.1	1/4	26	5.3
M7 × 1.0		6.0	5/16	18	6.5	5/16	22	6.8
M8 × 1.25		6.8	3/8	16	7.9	3/8	20	8.3
M10 × 1.5		8.5	7/16	14	9.3	7/16	18	9.7
M12 × 1.75		10.2	1/2	12	10.5	1/2	16	11.1
M14 × 2		12.0	9/16	12	12.0	9/16	16	14.0
M16 × 2		14.0	5/8	11	13.5	5/8	14	12.6

BA (British Association) Thread angle 47.5°			UNC (Unified Coarse) Thread angle 60°			UNF (Unified Fine) Thread angle 60°		
Designation	Pitch (tpi)	Tapping size (mm)	Major dia.	Pitch (tpi)	Tapping size (mm)	Major dia.	Pitch (tpi)	Tapping size (mm)
0	25.4	5.0	1/4	20	5.2	1/4	28	5.4
1	28.2	4.4	5/16	18	6.5	5/16	24	6.8
2	31.3	4.0	3/8	16	8	3/8	24	8.4
3	34.8	3.3	7/16	14	9.3	7/16	20	9.8
4	38.5	2.95	1/2	13	10.8	1/2	20	11.4
5	43.1	2.6	9/16	12	12.1	9/16	18	12.8
6	47.9	2.25	5/8	11	13.5	5/8	18	14.5

The sizes of the tapping drills listed above are the nearest convenient size larger than the threads core diameters
If you need to use an alternative drill use the next larger size

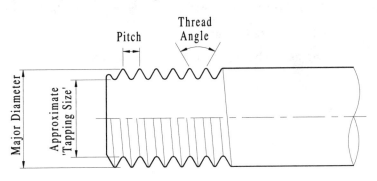

Chord lengths for PCDs

Number of holes	Pitch of holes on unit circle *	Number of holes	Pitch of holes on unit circle *
3	0.8660	17	0.2588
4	0.7071	18	0.2393
5	0.5878	19	0.2225
6	0.5000	20	0.2079
7	0.4339	21	0.1951
8	0.3827	22	0.1837
9	0.3420	23	0.1736
10	0.3090	24	0.1646
11	0.2817	25	0.1564
12	0.2588	30	0.1490
13	0.2393	35	0.1423
14	0.2225	40	0.1362
15	0.2079	45	0.1305
16	0.1951	50	0.1253

* To convert the pitch values into chord lengths for circles with a diameter other than one unit (i.e. 1 mm or 1 in), multiply the pitch circle diameter (PCD) by the number extracted from the table.

Example 1   *To find the chord length for marking out 7 holes on a 125 mm PCD*

$0.8677 \times 125 =$ **108.4625 mm**

This figure can be approximated to 108.5 mm

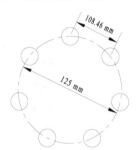

Example 2   *To find the chord length for marking out 5 holes on a 6 ½ in PCD*

$0.55878 \times 6\,½ =$ **3.8207 in**

This figure can be approximated to 3.82 in or $3^{13}/_{16}$ in.

Example first-angle projection

The isometric view of the pulley mount below has been redrawn in first-angle
orthographic projection in the frame at the bottom of the page. Imperial dimensions
are used, a sectional view is added and correct types of line are shown.

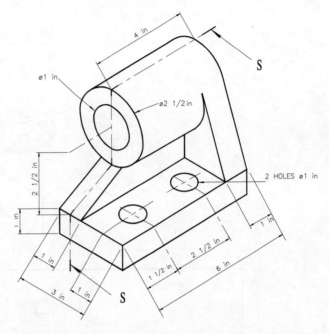

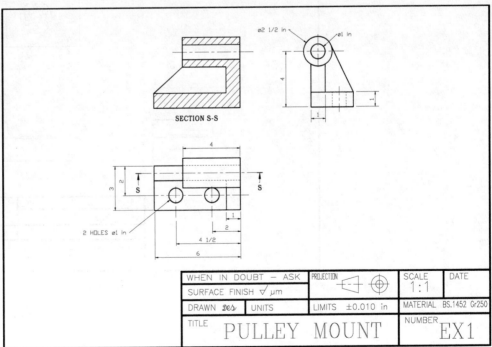

Example third-angle projection

The isometric view of the slideway below has been redrawn in third-angle orthographic projection in the frame at the bottom of the page. Metric dimensions are used and correct line types shown.

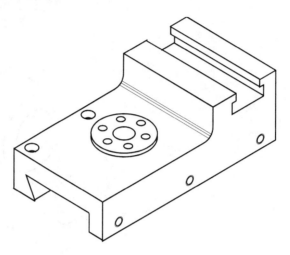

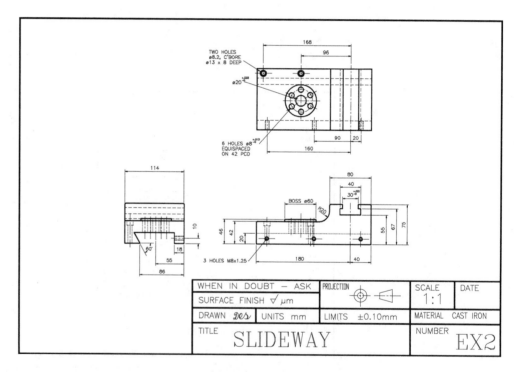

WHEN IN DOUBT – ASK	PROJECTION	SCALE 1:1	DATE
SURFACE FINISH ▽ μm			
DRAWN *des*	UNITS mm	LIMITS ±0.10mm	MATERIAL CAST IRON
TITLE SLIDEWAY		NUMBER EX2	

Requisition forms

Typical material and tool requisition forms are shown below. They are used for ordering equipment from the stores, they also enable the stores personnel to keep up to date records of stocks and their whereabouts. If you do not use standard forms in your workplace, you must fill in copies of these forms for all your material and tool requirements.

Materials requisition form

Material	Qty	Size	Job code	Date
Requested by		Approved by		

Tool requisition form

Tool	Job code	Loan date	Return date
Requested by	Loan approved by		

Repeat test

The multiple choice question paper will only be issued to candidates by their supervisor on satisfactory completion of the appropriate exercises. The answer sheet below must be completed by the candidate when the questions are issued.

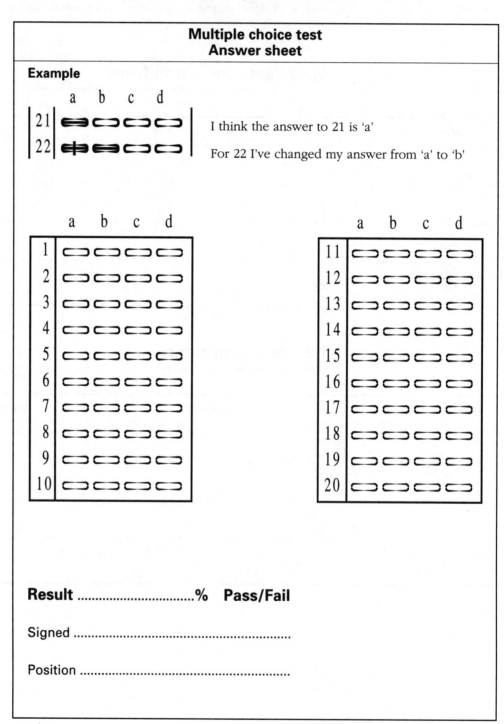

**Multiple choice test
Answer sheet**

Example

	a	b	c	d
21	⊜	⊂⊃	⊂⊃	⊂⊃	I think the answer to 21 is 'a'
22	⊕	⊜	⊂⊃	⊂⊃	For 22 I've changed my answer from 'a' to 'b'

Result ....% **Pass/Fail**

Signed ....

Position ....

Index